Roy Crane

WASH TUBBS
AND
CAPTAIN EASY
★ SOLDIER OF FORTUNE ★
VOLUME 16 (1940-1941)

by Roy Crane

BILL BLACKBEARD
Series Editor

Flying Buttress Classics Library

© NEA 1991
Wash Tubbs is a trademark of Newspaper Enterprise Association
A Flying Buttress Classics Library edition © NBM 1991
ISBN 1-56163-018-7 paperback
ISBN 1-56163-019-5 hardcover $35
LC 87-062174
Design by Bhob
Production: Rachael Rodrigo

FLYING BUTTRESS
Classics library

an imprint of

NBM

NANTIER · BEALL · MINOUSTCHINE
Publishing co.
new york

WASH TUBBS

ALTITUDE, 3000 FEET. TWO PEOPLE STRUGGLE FOR A GUN
YOU DOG! SWINE!
LEGGO THE WHEEL, YOU LITTLE FOOL! YOU'LL THROW US INTO A SPIN!
8-5
THERE! YOU'VE DONE IT! YOU'VE —
THUD!
SO YOU KNOCKED YOURSELF OUT! HA, HA! SERVES YOU RIGHT, MR. G-MAN
COPR. 1940 BY NEA SERVICE, INC. T. M. REG. U. S. PAT. OFF.
8-5
WITH EASY UNCONSCIOUS, IT SUDDENLY DAWNS ON HELGA THAT THERE IS NO ONE LEFT TO FLY THE PLANE BUT HERSELF... AND SHE DOESN'T KNOW HOW!

OUTSIDE IS TOTAL DARKNESS. EASY, THE PILOT, LIES ON THE FLOOR UNCONSCIOUS. ALONE AT THE CONTROLS SITS HELGA WOLFE, WHO HAS NEVER FLOWN SO MUCH AS A KITE BEFORE, TRYING DESPERATELY TO GET THE HANG OF THINGS
THEN IT HAPPENS—THE CRACKING CRASH OF TREES AND WINGS—A SCREAM OF TERROR —
8-6
THEN SILENCE!
Roy Crane
8-6
COPR. 1940 BY NEA SERVICE, INC. T. M. REG. U. S. PAT. OFF.

IT IS DAYLIGHT WHEN EASY CRAWLS FROM THE WRECKAGE OF THE PLANE
I THOUGHT YOU WERE DEAD
MAYBE I AM. I'M NOT SURE YET
8-7
I MADE QUITE A MESS OF THINGS. THERE'S NO TELLING WHERE WE ARE; AND I THINK MY ANKLE IS BROKEN
THEN I'D BETTER GO AFTER HELP
AND BRING BACK THE F.B.I? NO, MY FRIEND
Roy Crane
COPR. 1940 BY NEA SERVICE, INC. T. M. REG. U. S. PAT. OFF.
UPON THAT ONE THING I AM DETERMINED. IF I CANNOT LEAVE THIS PLACE, NEITHER WILL YOU!
8-7

EVEN WITH MY BROKEN ANKLE, PERHAPS IT IS NOT TOO LATE TO DISPOSE OF THIS ACCURSED G-MAN IN SUCH A MANNER THAT HIS DEATH WILL BE BLAMED ON THE CRASH. LET ME THINK
8-8
I FEAR I AM HURT WORSE THAN I THOUGHT. THERE IS A PAIN IN MY CHEST. YOU WILL HELP ME TO THE HOSPITAL, YES?
CERTAINLY... IF YOU'LL PUT DOWN THAT GUN
AH, YOU ARE AFRAID. YOU DON' TRUS' LITTLE HELGA. THIS PAIN IN MY CHEST... IT IS GROWING WORSE. I CANNOT LIE DOWN ALONE... PLEASE COME CLOSER, SEE IF YOU CAN HELP ME
EASY HESITATES, FOR HE SEES THE GLITTER IN HER EYES, THE SLY, SARDONIC SMILE
8-8
SEE? I WILL THROW THE GUN ASIDE. INJURED AS I AM, I CANNOT REACH IT
T. M. REG. U. S. PAT. OFF.
COPR. 1940 BY NEA SERVICE, INC.
SEE? I WILL LAY THE GUN OUT OF REACH. OH, PLEASE TRY TO HELP ME! THIS PAIN IN MY CHEST... IT IS ALMOST MORE THAN I CAN BEAR
BEND CLOSER... PUT YOUR ARMS ABOUT ME... PERHAPS IF YOU WILL LIF' ME TO A MORE COMFORTABLE POSITION... THERE!
8-9
NOW, MY FOOL!
COPR. 1940 BY NEA SERVICE, INC.
8-9
WARY AS EVER, EASY DUCKS THE WELL AIMED ROCK JUST IN TIME
AND HELGA, IN A RAGE AT BEING OUTWITTED AGAIN, SEIZES THE GUN AND FIRES!
BANG!
T. M. REG. U. S. PAT. OFF.
KA-POW! POW!
8-10
EASY COUNTS SIX SHOTS, THEN RISES.
THAT'S THAT
CLICK
COPR. 1940 BY NEA SERVICE, INC.
FROM NOW ON, WE'LL DO THINGS MY WAY, WHICH MEANS YOU'RE GOING TO JAIL ON THIS WHEELBARROW I'M MAKING
8-10
T. M. REG. U. S. PAT. OFF.

9

THOUSANDS OF MAPS AND PICTURES! BY GEORGE, EASY, I BELIEVE WE'VE FOUND THE ACTUAL HEADQUARTERS OF THOSE FOREIGN AGENTS!
9-15
DISTINCTLY I HEARD THE CLICK OF A DOOR UPSTAIRS, COMRADE
AND STRANGE FOOTSTEPS! WE HAD BETTER INVESTIGATE
THEN UP THE SECRET PASSAGE
COPR. 1940 BY NEA SERVICE, INC. T. M. REG. U. S. PAT. OFF.
AH, HA! IT'S JUST AS I THOUGHT! A G-MAN !!
AND LOOK! THE OTHER IS THAT TRAITOR OF A PILOT WHOM HELGA WAS TO DESTROY—SOMETHING HAS GONE WRONG!
9-15
ROY CRANE

SO THAT IS HIS REAL NAME... 'EASY!' OH, WAT FOOLS WE WERE TO ACCEPT HIM AS A PILOT TO ASSIST IN OUR GLORIOUS WORK OF ESPIONAGE!
THEY 'AVE DISCOVER' OUR MAPS AND PICTURES OF VITAL AMERICAN INDUSTRIES
AND OUR RECORDS! OUR PRICELESS RECORDS! OUR CODES AND EVERYTHING!
COMRADE, IF OUR GREAT ORGANIZATION IS TO SURVIVE IN AMERICA, THESE G-MEN MUS' BE DESTROY' NOW! AT ONCE!
8-16
BOT NOT WIS A GUN — IT IS TOO MOCH RISK
BETTER IT IS TO USE GASOLINE
8-16
ROY CRANE
AND NOW HOW SHALL WE CONTRIVE TO IGNITE IT SO THOSE ACCURSED G-MEN WILL BE HOPELESSLY TRAPPED?
WITH THIS!
COPR. 1940 BY NEA SERVICE, INC. T. M. REG. U. S. PAT. OFF.

AH! HERE IS HERMAN
SHHH! TWO G-MEN ARE IN THE NEXT ROOM, HERMAN. FOR THE GOOD OF THE CAUSE WE ARE PREPARING TO DESTROY EVERYTHING, ESPECIALLY THOSE G-MEN
I HEAR VOICES!
HMM! MAYBE WE AREN'T ALONE AFTER ALL, EASY. LET'S GO DOWNSTAIRS AND INVESTIGATE
8-17
THAT'S FUNNY. THE VOICES SEEM TO BE UPSTAIRS, YET THERE APPEARS TO BE NO WAY OF GETTING THERE EXCEPT BY THE LADDER
AND THERE'S NO DOOR FROM THAT ROOM TO ANY OTHER
IN THAT CASE, OLD TIMER, WE'LL LOCK ALL THE EXITS AND SEND FOR HELP. IF ANY SECRET AGENTS ARE HERE, I'M TAKING NO CHANCES OF THEIR GETTING AWAY!
8-17
T. M. REG. U. S. PAT. OFF.
COPR. 1940 BY NEA SERVICE, INC.

11

NOT BAD, EASY. SIX KNOWN FOREIGN AGENTS IN THIS AREA ARE DEAD OR UNDER ARREST, INCLUDING THE LEADER, HELGA WOLFE. NATURALLY, I'VE FILED A REPORT GIVING YOU DUE CREDIT FOR THE PART YOU PLAYED
I DIDN'T DO MUCH
8-22
NEVERTHELESS, THERE'S A CERTAIN HIGH GOVERNMENT OFFICIAL IN WASHINGTON WHO'D LIKE TO... AH... MAKE YOUR ACQUAINTANCE
YOU'RE KIDDING
JUST TO PROVE I'M NOT, HERE'S A TICKET ON THE 5:30 PLANE... YOU'RE TO GO TO THIS ADDRESS FOR DINNER AND ASK FOR BAKED FROG LEGS
BUT WHAT ABOUT MY JOB WITH McKEE INDUSTRIES?
COPR. 1940 BY NEA SERVICE, INC. T. M. REG. U. S. PAT. OFF.
THE SUBJECT OF THIS CONFERENCE, EASY, IS CONSIDERED MORE IMPORTANT THAN YOUR CONFOUNDED JOB IN THE POWDER PUFF DEPARTMENT!
CAB'S WAITING, CAPTAIN EASY
8-22

WASHINGTON, D.C.:
OF ALL THE DIZZY WAYS TO CONTACT A HIGH GOVERNMENT OFFICIAL... I'M TO GO IN THIS RESTAURANT AND ASK FOR BAKED FROG-LEGS
THEY AREN'T ON THE MENU, SIR. ARE YOU SURE YOU'D LIKE BAKED FROG LEGS?
YES. BAKED FROGLEGS
8-23
VERY WELL, CAPTAIN EASY. YOUR CAR WILL BE WAITING FOR YOU AS SOON AS YOU'RE THRU
?
8-23
WELL, WELL! THIS IS ALL VERY MYSTERIOUS
YES, SIR. OUR INSTRUCTIONS WERE TO TAKE EVERY PRECAUTION TO SEE THAT YOU WEREN'T FOLLOWED, SIR
COPR. 1940 BY NEA SERVICE, INC. T. M. REG. U. S. PAT. OFF
Roy Crane

THE CAR DARTS INTO ONE OF THE BIG GOVERNMENT BUILDINGS. EASY DOESN'T KNOW WHICH ONE.
THEN HE'S TAKEN UP A PRIVATE ELEVATOR, AND THRU SEVERAL DOORS HAVING NO NAMES OR NUMBERS
8-24
AND INTO AN OFFICE:
CAPTAIN EASY, I BELIEVE
YES, SUH
COPR. 1940 BY NEA SERVICE, INC. T. M. REG. U. S. PAT. OFF
Roy Crane
PERHAPS YOU THINK ALL THIS SECRECY IS CRAZY, AND PERHAPS IT IS. YET NO DEPARTMENT OF THE GOVERNMENT IS SO CLOSELY WATCHED AS THE VARIED BRANCHES OF THE SECRET SERVICE. SIT DOWN, YOUNG MAN. I'D LIKE TO TALK TO YOU
8-24

13

14

September 1940

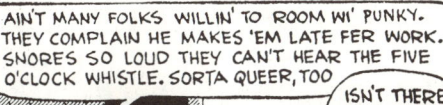

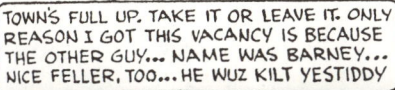

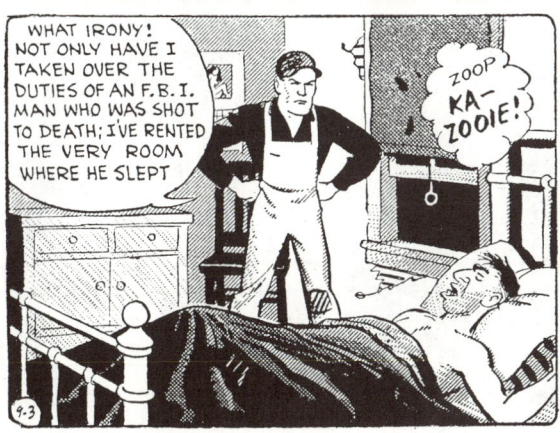

16

17

AND NOW COMES THE BONUS, COMRADES. WAN HONNER DOLLAR EACH. HA, HA! OLD POPS IS MIGHTY FINE FELLA WHEN IT IS TIME FOR THE BONUS, YES?
THAT'S DIRT CHEAP FOR WOT WE DONE
IT'S GOOD ENOUGH FOR AN ESCAPED CONVICT WITH A RECORD LIKE YOURS, PUNKY FOWLER. TAKE IT OR LEAVE IT
HUMPH!
HEY! WHERE'D YA GIT THIS MONEY?
MAYBE IT IS NOT GOOD ENOUGH FOR YOU, HEY?
COPR. 1939 BY NEA SERVICE, INC. T. M. REG. U. S. PAT. OFF.
THIS DOLLAR BILL! LOOK ON THE BACK— THERE'S WRITIN' ON IT!
$1
9-12

THE MONEY? PART OF IT I OBTAIN FROM THE DESK OF THAT F. B. I. MAN WHO— AH—WAS DISPOSE OF LAST NIGHT. WHY?
I KNEW IT! LOOK AT THE WRITIN' ON THE BACK OF THIS DOLLAR BILL—IT'S A SECRET MESSAGE
9-13
"HAVE SECURED JOB IN SHIPYARD. ROOMING WITH A MAN NAMED PUNKY FOWLER, 322 MAIN ST. AT YOUR SERVICE." SIGNED, "SPECIAL AGENT Z-1."
SPECIAL AGENT Z-I. HMM! IT APPEAR THERE IS ANOTHER G-MAN IN OUR MIDST.
HE'S THAT HOOK-NOSED GUY ROOMIN' WITH ME! I SUSPECTED HIM ALL ALONG
HE'S BEEN SENT TO CATCH US!
AH, YES! BOT I WOULDN' BECOME ALARM, PUNKY, FOR WE 'AVE MADE THE DISCOVERY IN AMPLE TIME
COPR. 1939 BY NEA SERVICE, INC. T. M. REG. U. S. PAT. OFF.

HA! NOW THAT WE'VE DISCOVERED THAT HOOK-NOSED ROOMMATE OF MINE'S A G-MAN, I KNOW HOW TO HANDLE HIM!
FOR THE PRESENT, PUNKY, PLEASE... NO SHOOTING!
WHAT! WE AIN'T GONNA SHOOT TH' BABOON LIKE WE DONE THEM OTHERS?
SHHH. NO SHOUTING, YOU FOOL! IN ESPIONAGE WORK, ONE LEARNS TO WHISPER
9-14
BUT THE FIRE! THEM KILLINGS! I GOTTA PENITENTIARY RECORD! SAY, LISSEN! YOU DON'T EXPECT ME TO SLEEP WITH NO G-MAN?
MOS' CERTAINLY, YES!
9-14
IF HE CAN SPY ON US, WE CAN ALSO SPY ON HIM. WE WILL LEARN HIS ASSOCIATES. WE WILL PREPARE FALSE CLUES BY THE SCORE. AH! WAT A MERRY CHASE WE WILL LEAD THIS SECRET AGENT
COPR. 1939 BY NEA SERVICE, INC. T. M. REG. U. S. PAT. OFF.

19

20

21

HI, HO—NO JOB, NO MONEY. SEEMS SILLY, HOLDING THIS PAPER OVER ME ANY LONGER... I'M SOAKING WET
WHY DIDN'T I KNOW ABOUT THIS PLACE? I COULD HAVE SAVED MY OTHER NICKEL AND HAD A PLACE TO SLEEP!
ALL NIGHT MOVIE 10¢
9-26
EVERYTHING LOOKS SO GOOD TO EAT. I...
I BEG YOUR PARDON, MISS. CAN I BE OF ASSISTANCE?
NO THANKS. I LIKE THE RAIN
NONSENSE! I'VE BEEN WATCHING YOU FOR SOME TIME. NOW SUPPOSE WE GO INSIDE AND HAVE SOMETHING TO EAT WHERE IT'S NICE AND WARM? I HAVE A JOB YOU MIGHT BE INTERESTED IN
9-26

FEELING BETTER, NOW THAT YOU'VE EATEN?
YOU BET. MAYBE YOU'VE NEVER BEEN BROKE AND KNOWN WHAT IT MEANS TO BE HUNGRY, MISTER... I MEAN **REALLY** HUNGRY, LIKE I WAS
OF COURSE I HAVE— WHAT'S YOUR TROUBLE, MISS?
DO YOU WANT THE TRUTH, OR A NICE BED-TIME STORY?
9-27
THE TRUTH
I'M VICKI SHERIDAN, JUST OUT OF THE HOME FOR CORRECTION... THE PENITENTIARY FOR DAMES, IN OTHER WORDS. MY MONEY RAN OUT. I COULDN'T GET A JOB, AND I WAS DESPERATE... I WAS SO DESPERATE AND HUNGRY I'D HAVE DONE ANYTHING
9-27
WELL, MISS SHERIDAN, IF YOU'RE STILL THAT DESPERATE, I BELIEVE I HAVE A JOB FOR YOU AT $35 A WEEK. HOW DOES THAT SOUND?
YOU'D BETTER NOT BE KIDDING, BUDDY—I **ACCEPT!**
COPR. 1939 BY NEA SERVICE, INC. T. M. REG. U. S. PAT. OFF.

I FOUND HER, CHIEF. SHE'S A GIRL JUST OUT OF THE HOME FOR CORRECTION. SHE'S CLEVER, PRETTY, AND **DESPERATE** FOR A JOB
HMM. NOT BAD
9-28
HOWEVER, WE CANNOT AFFORD TO TAKE CHANCES WITH ANYONE WHO MIGHT BE A FEDERAL AGENT, LUGWIT. YOU'D BETTER CHECK HER STORY WITH THE HOME FOR CORRECTION
LATER:
EVERYTHING SHE SAID IS TRUE, CHIEF. SHE WAS CONVICTED OF SHOPLIFTING AND GOT OUT MONDAY
VERY GOOD, LUGWIT! VERY GOOD!
T. M. REG. U. S. PAT. OFF.
COPR. 1940 BY NEA SERVICE, INC.
A BLONDE! PRETTY AND PETITE! JUST THE RIGHT TYPE!
NEXT DAY, VICKI SHERIDAN IS MET IN HOGSHEAD BY THE FOREIGN AGENT IN CHARGE OF SHIPYARD SABOTAGE
9-28

October 1940

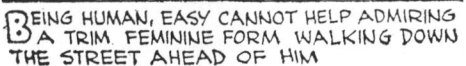

IT WAS SO GALLANT OF YOU TO RESCUE ME FROM THAT AWFUL PERSON! I'M AFRAID YOU'VE WON THE UNDYING GRATITUDE OF A VERY LONELY LITTLE GIRL
IF HE BOTHERS YOU ANY MORE, MISS, JUST LET ME KNOW
HOW SWEET OF YOU! HOW CONSIDERATE! I'M VICKI SHERIDAN. I DO HOPE YOU'LL COME TO SEE ME
HOW ABOUT TONIGHT?
10-3
OH, THAT WOULD BE DARLING! I'LL BE THRU WORK AT FIVE
I'LL BE HERE
AH, HA! ROMANCE IN THE BUD, PUNKY! OUR PLAN IS A BRILLIANT SUCCESS
THAT DUMB G-MAN NEVER SUSPECTED THAT VICKI WAS ONE OF US
10-3
COPR. 1940 BY NEA SERVICE, INC. T. M. REG. U. S. PAT. OFF.

AS EASY ARRIVES AT THE ELITE BEAUTY PARLOR, PUNKY FOWLER SLINKS OUT
ELITE BEAUTY SHOP
?
!
ELITE BEAUTY SHOP
10-4
THAT FELLOW BEEN BOTHERING YOU AGAIN, VICKI?
HE'S HORRIBLE! ALL THE MEN IN THIS TOWN ARE HORRIBLE! OH, I'M SO GLAD YOU CAME, EASY! I DON'T BELIEVE I'D HAVE HAD THE NERVE TO WALK HOME ALONE
10-4
LISTEN, IF YOU WANT ME TO TAKE A SOCK AT FOWLER—
OH, NO! PLEASE DON'T HAVE ANY TROUBLE WITH HIM. HE'S DANGEROUS! WHY, I HEARD THAT HE'S SUSPECTED OF MURDER!
COPR. 1940 BY NEA SERVICE, INC. T. M. REG. U. S. PAT. OFF.

WHO TOLD YOU THAT PUNKY FOWLER WAS SUSPECTED OF MURDER?
WHY, EVERYBODY SAYS SO. THEY SAY HE KILLED A G-MAN, AND THAT HE'S A TRAITOR BEING PAID BY SOME FOREIGN GOVERNMENT TO SABOTAGE THE SHIPYARD
10-5
BUT WHY DON'T THE POLICE PUT HIM IN JAIL? DOESN'T ANYBODY CARE WHAT HAPPENS? HAVEN'T THEY ANY PATRIOTISM?
BELIEVE ME, IF I WAS A MAN I'D DO SOMETHING! I MAY ANYWAY. HOW DOES A PERSON GO ABOUT CATCHING A SPY, EASY?
EH? WHY, I-AH- DON'T KNOW MUCH ABOUT IT
10-5
BUT YOU'RE AN AMERICAN! YOU'RE SMART. YOU'RE PATRIOTIC. LISTEN, EASY. WHY DON'T WE BOTH GET THE GOODS ON THAT GUY?
HMM! I WONDER IF I DARE TELL THIS GIRL WHO I REALLY AM?
COPR. 1940 BY NEA SERVICE, INC. T. M. REG. U. S. PAT. OFF.

25

26

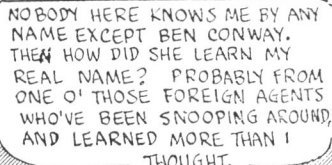

27

28

YOU THINK WE ARE FINISHED, YES? HA, HA! WE SHALL SEE!
YES, GO AHEAD AND CALL THE COPS, YA FLATFOOT— THERE'S THE TELEPHONE
THANKS
10-21
EASY LIFTS THE RECEIVER AND....
COPR. 1940 BY NEA SERVICE, INC. T. M. REG. U. S. PAT. OFF.
HAW, HAW! LITTLE DID HE DREAM THE TELEPHONE WAS A DUMMY TO TRAP SUCH FOOLS AS HE
HO, HO, HO!
?
10-21
ROY CRANE

PUSH YOUR CHAIR OVER TO MINE, POPS... THAT'S IT... NOW WE CAN UNTIE EACH OTHER
AH, EXCELLENT!
HA, HA! LITTLE DID HE REALIZE THAT TWO OTHER G-MEN 'AVE FALLEN THRU THAT TRAP DOOR BEFORE HIM, AND THEIR BODIES FOUND IN THE STREETS!
10-22
GOOD HEAVENS! SURELY YOU AREN'T GOING TO MURDER EASY?
EASY, EH? IS THAT HIS NAME?
WELL, ER-
WHY, THE MAN WHO BROUGHT DESTRUCTION TO HELGA WOLFE IN DISTRICT TWO—YES, I AM POSITIVE! HIS NAME WAS EASY! HA, HA! YOU MAY REST ASSURED, MY LITTLE KITTEN—HE WILL MOLEST OUR GLORIOUS ORGANIZATION NO MORE
ROY CRANE
10-22
COPR. 1940 BY NEA SERVICE, INC. T. M. REG. U. S. PAT. OFF.

THE CELLAR IS ESPECIALLY PREPARE', SO THAT NO ONE, NOT EVEN EASY, CAN ESCAPE
AN' WOT'S MORE, I'LL TAKE AN EXTRY PRECAUTION
OH, NO! PLEASE!
10-23
THE LITTLE LADY IS RIGHT, PUNKY. NO SHOOTING
WHAT?
OUR TASK, MY DEAR PUNKY, IS TO DELAY THE CONSTRUCTION OF DESTROYERS. TONIGHT THE SHIPYARD WILL SUFFER A PARALYZING DISASTER
HOWEVER, SINCE WE WILL 'AVE NO FURTHER USE FOR THESE QUARTERS, WHAT A DROLL JOKE IF, BY ACCIDENT, SOME ONE FORGOT AND LEF' A THERMITE BOMB BEHIND
HA! I GETCHA, POPS
SURE, HAVE A NICE LITTLE BONFIRE!
10-23
COPR. 1940 BY NEA SERVICE, INC. T. M. REG. U. S. PAT. OFF.

HERE, YOU AND VICKI WILL TAKE THE RECORDS, CODES, AND FORMULAS AND PLACE THEM IN THE CAR IN PREPARATION FOR THE GETAWAY
10-24
AND NOW, PUNKY, OUR TIME IS SHORT. ALREADY THE TRAIN HAS ARRIVE'. SOON THE SWITCH ENGINE WILL MOVE THE CARS INTO THE SHIPYARD
ARE THE BOMBS READY AND SAFELY CONCEAL IN THE LUMPS OF IMITATION COAL?
ALL EXCEPT THIS'N I'M LEAVIN' BEHIND FOR THAT G-MAN
COPR. 1940 BY NEA SERVICE, INC. T. M. REG. U. S. PAT. OFF.
THEN WE WILL LOCK UP MOS' CARE-FULLY. IT WOULD NEVER DO FOR ANY-ONE TO BREAK IN AND RESCUE HIM FROM THE CELLAR! OH, NO!
ROY CRANE
10-24
10-25
AN INNOCENT-LOOKING PIPE HAS BEEN LEFT IN THE HOUSE WHERE EASY IS A PRISONER. IT CONTAINS THERMITE WHICH, UPON IGNITION, GENERATES HEAT OF 3,000 DEGREES AND CANNOT BE EXTINGUISHED BY ORDINARY FIRE-FIGHTING METHODS
IS EASY PANIC-STRICKEN? NO, INDEED!
JUST A HUNCH— I'LL BET A COOKIE VICKI COMES BACK TO RESCUE ME
MEANWHILE, VICKI AND A FOREIGN AGENT ARE PRE-PARING FOR A GETAWAY
ARE THESE RECORDS REALLY IMPORTANT?
I'LL SAY THEY ARE, KIDDO! THEY COULD SEND US ALL TO THE KLINK FOR THE RESTA OUR LIVES
COPR. 1940 BY NEA SERVICE, INC. T. M. REG. U. S. PAT. OFF.
THANKS—I JUST WANTED TO MAKE SURE
KONK!
ROY CRANE
10-25
10-26
PULLING A DOZEN CARS OF COAL, A SWITCH ENGINE CHUGS ITS WAY TOWARD THE SHIPYARD
THREE MEN LOITER UNNOTICED ON THE BRIDGE JUST AHEAD
OPEN THE SACK, PUNKY
ROY CRANE
10-26
COPR. 1940 BY NEA SERVICE, INC. T. M. REG. U. S. PAT. OFF.
THERE! WE DROP THE IMITATION COAL ONTO EVER' PASSING CAR. HA, HA! WHO WOULD SUSPECT' THAT EACH CONCEALS A DANGER-OUS INCENDIARY BOMB?
PLUMP!

31

November 1940

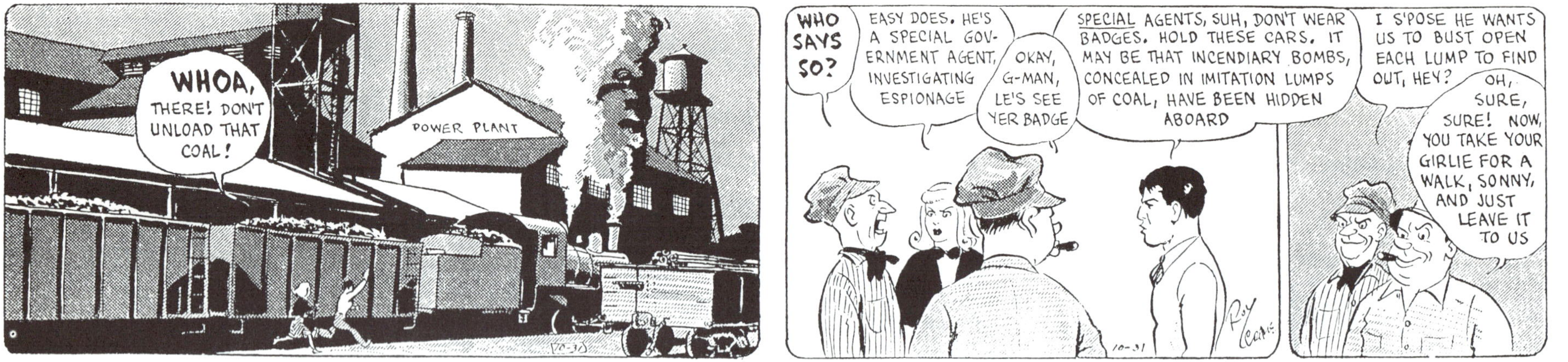

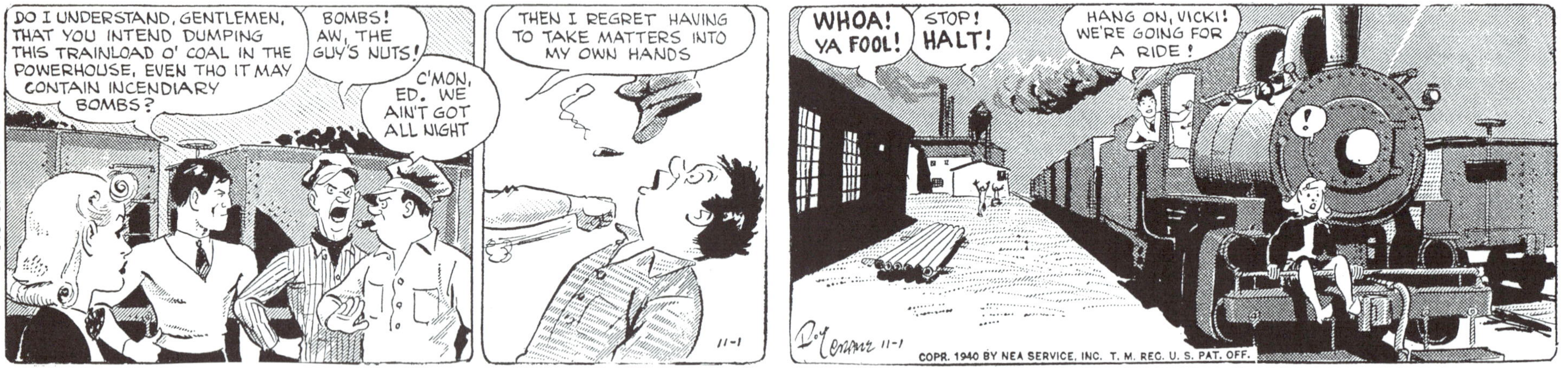

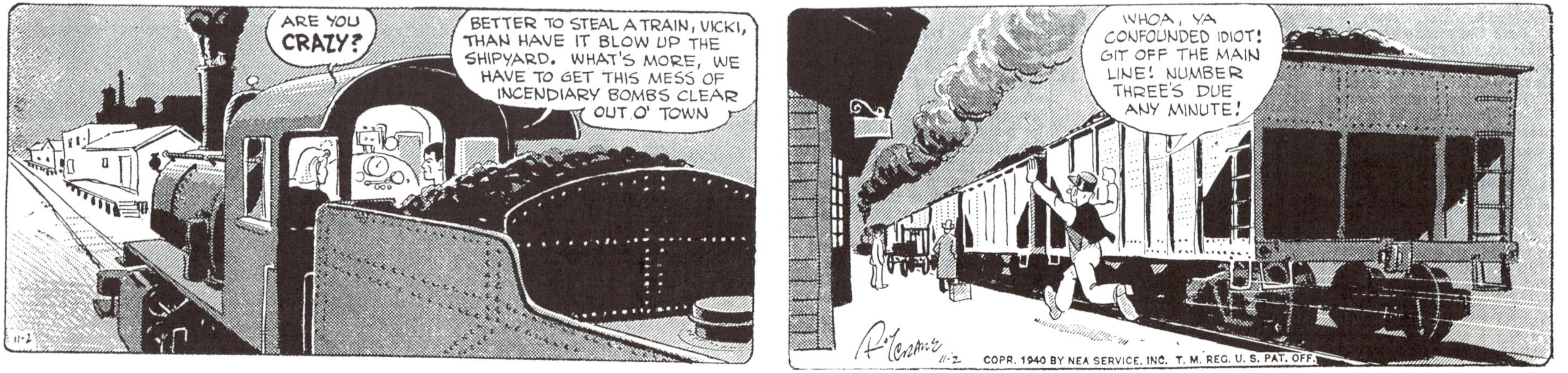

33

34

35

36

37

MY SIDE OF THE STORY IS RATHER BRIEF. MY SECRETARY, MISS ZAVISH, CALLED ONE EVENING WITH SOME DOCUMENTS AND LEFT, SAYING SHE WAS GOING TO A MOVIE. AS TO HER MURDER, I KNOW NOTHING
YOUR BUTLER TESTIFIED HE HEARD YOU AND MISS ZAVISH QUARRELING, MR. DRINK-WATER
HE'S A LIAR! THAT'S WHY I FIRED HIM
11-21
HMM! AND HOW DID YOU EXPLAIN TO THE POLICE THE BLOODSTAINS ON YOUR CAR AND CLOTHES?
I DIDN'T! THERE IS NO EXPLANATION FOR SOMETHING ONE KNOWS ABSO-LUTELY NOTHING ABOUT
THE SAME IS TRUE OF MY PISTOL.. IT JUST DISAPPEARED. I KNOW NOT WHERE, OR HOW, AND I CANNOT EXPLAIN
COPR. 1940 BY NEA SERVICE, INC. T. M. REG. U. S. PAT. OFF.
11-21

YOU'VE ASKED A LOT OF VERY PERSONAL QUESTIONS, YOUNG MAN, AND I FAIL TO SEE WHERE FOREIGN ESPIONAGE HAS ANYTHING TO DO WITH THE EFFORTS OF THE POLICE TO INVOLVE ME IN THE MURDER OF MY SECRETARY
PERHAPS, AS THE DISTRICT ATTORNEY SAYS, SUH, WE ARE BARKING UP THE WRONG TREE
HOW-EVER...
EH?, WHAT'S THAT, GWENDOLYN?
THAT MAN, MR. DRINKWATER.. HE'S ON THE PHONE AGAIN. HE SAYS YOU BETTER TALK, TOO
11-22
ANY COPS AT YOUR HOUSE, DRINKWATER?
WHY... WHY, NO!
COPR. 1940 BY NEA SERVICE, INC.
THA'S FINE! SWELL! I'LL BE OVER IN THREE MINUTES. GOTTA LITTLE SURPRISE FOR YA, PALLY. AN' BELIEVE ME, IF YOU THINK YOU'RE IN HOT WATER NOW, YA AIN'T SEEN NOTHIN' YET!!
!
T. M. REG. U. S. PAT. OFF.
11-22

SOME PERSON WAS MAKING THREATS TO ME OVER THE PHONE... HE'S COMING ANY MINUTE
IF YOU DON'T MIND, MR. DRINKWATER, WE'LL STEP INTO A CLOSET
HI, YA, PALLY! WELL, THERE AIN'T NO USE TO BEAT AROUND THE BUSH
THE-AH-GENTLEMAN IS HERE, MR. DRINK-WATER
11-23
HERE'S A PHOTOSTAT OF A LETTER AGREEIN' TO TURN OVER ALL PLANS AND SPECIFICATIONS OF MILITARY PLANES TO A CERTAIN UNFRIENDLY FOREIGN POWER... AND SIGNED BY YOU!
A FORGERY!
11-23
COPR. 1940 BY NEA SERVICE, INC. T. M. REG. U. S. PAT. OFF.
TAKE A CLOSER LOOK, CHUM! IT'S ON YER OWN PERSONAL STATIONERY. AN' I BIN ASSURED THERE AIN'T A HANDWRITIN' EXPERT ON EARTH BUT WOT'D PRO-CLAIM IT GENU-WINE
!

39

WHEN EASY LEAVES MR. DRINKWATER'S:
FOLLOW THAT OTHER TAXI, BUT DON'T LET 'EM KNOW IT!
THE FIRST CAB PASSES AN ALLEY
WUP! THERE'S THE SIGNAL. PINKY'S BEING TRAILED
TAXI
11-28
A MOMENT LATER, WHEN EASY'S CAB STOPS AT A TRAFFIC LIGHT:
WHUMP!
WHY DONCHA LOOK WHERE YA GOIN'?
DREADFULLY SORRY. ALL MY FAULT. I'LL GLADLY PAY ANY DAMAGES
AND THE BLACK-MAILER GETS AWAY. HMM! I'LL JUST TAKE THIS FELLA'S NUMBER AND SEE WHO HE IS
ROY CRANE
11-28
COPR. 1940 BY NEA SERVICE, INC. T. M. REG. U. S. PAT. OFF.

EASY DELIVERS A PHONY PACKAGE, AS AN EXCUSE TO TALK WITH DRINK-WATER'S NEW SECRETARY
I'LL PUT IT AWAY FOR HIM
THANKS. BY THE WAY, MISS WENTZ, HOW DO YOU LIKE WORKING FOR THE OLD BOY?
11-29
OH, FINE. ONLY I HARDLY EVER SEE HIM. EVEN BEFORE HE BECAME ILL, HE WAS AWAY ON HIS BICYCLE MOST OF THE TIME
HIS BICYCLE?
HE'S A CARD. HE RIDES AROUND THE FACTORY ON A BIKE TO SAVE TIME. THE MINUTE HE FINISHES HIS MORNING DICTATION, AWAY HE GOES!
DOESN'T HE EVEN RETURN TO SIGN HIS MAIL?
ROY CRANE
COPR. 1940 BY NEA SERVICE, INC. T. M. REG. U. S. PAT. OFF.
11-29
OH, NO! WE SEND IT TO HIM BY WILLIE, THE OFFICE BOY. WHEN WILLIE RUNS HIM DOWN, MR. DRINKWATER'S OFTEN TOO BUSY TO BOTHER
AH! AN IMPORTANT FACT! DRINKWATER IS SO ABSORBED IN ENGINEERING PROB-LEMS HE'S CARELESS ABOUT SIGNING HIS LETTERS!

DISTRICT ATTORNEY'S OFFICE:
MIGHTY GLAD YOU DROPPED IN, OLD MAN. YES, INDEED. HAVE GREAT NEWS. THE POLICE HAVE UNEARTHED SOME RATHER CONCLUSIVE EVIDENCE THAT JUST ABOUT CLINCHES THE CASE ON DRINKWATER
WHAT SORT OF EVIDENCE?
11-30
FOUND HIS PISTOL. TRACED THE REGISTRATION NUMBER... THERE'S NO MISTAKE ABOUT ITS BEING HIS. AND THE BALLISTIC TEST PROVES THAT THE SHOT WHICH KILLED HIS SECRETARY WAS FIRED FROM THAT GUN!
BUT WERE HIS FINGER-PRINTS FOUND ON IT?
WELL, AH, THAT'S A MERE DETAIL. THE FINGERPRINTS WERE TOO BLURRED TO BE OF ANY REAL VALUE. BUT THE BLOODSTAINS, AND EVERYTHING ELSE, POINT TO HIS GUILT. WE'RE TO MAKE AN ARREST IMMEDIATELY
COPR. 1940 BY NEA SERVICE, INC. T. M. REG. U. S. PAT. OFF.
11-30
YOU'D BE MAKING A MISTAKE, SUH. I HAVE REASON TO BELIEVE THAT DRINKWATER'S BEEN FRAMED BY FOREIGN AGENTS
!

BEFORE YOU ARREST DRINKWATER, SUH, I'D LIKE ENOUGH TIME TO RUN DOWN A FEW CLUES
WHAT REASON HAVE YOU TO THINK HE'S BEEN FRAMED ?
BECAUSE FOREIGN AGENTS HAVE BEEN BUSY TRYING TO DESTROY SUCH VITAL COGS IN OUR PREPAREDNESS PROGRAM AS T.X. DRINKWATER
12-2
ALSO, THE CHIEF WITNESS AGAINST HIM IS HIS EX-BUTLER, WHO, IN HIS POSITION, COULD EASILY HAVE STOLEN DRINKWATER'S GUN AND PLANTED BLOODSTAINS ON HIS CLOTHES AND CAR
HMM!
WHAT REASON HAVE YOU TO SUSPECT THIS BUTLER ?
WELL, FOR ONE THING, I LOST THE TRAIL OF ANOTHER SUSPECT WHEN MY TAXI WAS STRUCK BY A BLUE SEDAN. THE LICENSE NUMBER OF THAT BLUE SEDAN WAS ISSUED TO DRINKWATER'S EX-BUTLER!
COPR. 1940 BY NEA SERVICE, INC. T. M. REG. U. S. PAT. OFF.
Roy Crane
12-2

HOW UTTERLY FANTASTIC! SURELY, YOUNG MAN, IF A FOREIGN AGENT WISHED TO HINDER PRODUCTION AT DRINKWATER AIRCRAFT, HE WOULDN'T TRY TO DO IT BY DISGRACING T.X. DRINKWATER... HE'D PLANT A BOMB!
NOT NECESSARILY, SUH
12-3
SABOTAGE IS THE ART OF FOUL PLAY. ANYTHING GOES! IF A SABOTEUR CAN CAUSE MORE DAMAGE BY WRECKING A MAN THAN A MACHINE, HE'LL DO IT!
FIRES AND EXPLOSIONS ARE TOO SPECTACULAR. LIKE A RAT IN A CRACKER BARREL, HE WREAKS MOST OF HIS DESTRUCTION UNSEEN. THE MOST DANGEROUS FORM OF SABOTAGE, AND THE HARDEST TO COMBAT, IS THAT WHICH DESTROYS NATIONAL LEADERSHIP AND MORALE. THAT'S WHAT WE'RE UP AGAINST
Roy Crane
12-3 COPR. 1940 BY NEA SERVICE, INC. T. M. REG. U. S. PAT. OFF.

BUT ALL THIS SPY-MENACE STUFF IS RIDICU-LOUS
HAVE YOU EVER HEARD OF THE DOSSIER SYSTEM? NO? IT ORIGINATED IN FRANCE, AND WAS A HUGE "POLICE RECORD," WHICH INCLUDED NOT ONLY CRIMINALS, BUT ALL PERSONS WHO MIGHT EVER BE WANTED BY THE POLICE
25 YEARS AGO THE SECRET SERVICE OF A CERTAIN COUNTRY APPLIED THE DOSSIER SYSTEM TO THE PEOPLE OF OTHER COUNTRIES. IT INCLUDED THOUSANDS OF NAMES... MEN AND WOMEN OF RENOWN, SOLDIERS, POLITICIANS, AND CRIMINALS!
12-4
BUT WHAT A RECORD! MORAL DELINQUENCIES! CRIMES! FAMILY SKELETONS! IN SHORT, IT WAS AN ENCYCLOPEDIA OF SCANDAL OF EVERY-ONE WHO MIGHT BE MADE USE OF BY BLACK-MAILING METHODS!
COPR. 1940 BY NEA SERVICE, INC.
TODAY, MR. LAGEL, AN IMPROVED DOSSIER SYSTEM IS BEING OPERATED BY THAT SAME COUNTRY IN NORTH AND SOUTH AMERICA! TERRIFIC PRESSURE IS BEING APPLIED BY FOREIGN AGENTS. AND T.X. DRINKWATER IS BUT ONE OF THE VICTIMS!
Roy Crane
12-4 T. M. REG. U. S. PAT. OFF.

PERSONALLY, MY DEAR BOY, I THINK YOU G-MEN ARE IMAGINING THINGS. SABOTAGING INDUSTRY BY BLACKMAIL... WELL, FRANKLY, IT SOUNDS RIDICULOUS
HOWEVER, I REALIZE DRINKWATER'S IMPORTANCE IN THE PREPAREDNESS PROGRAM. GLAD TO COOPERATE. YOU HAVE MY WORD THAT HE'LL NOT BE ARRESTED UNTIL YOU'VE HAD A REASONABLE CHANCE TO INVESTIGATE
THANKS
BLAZES! THAT'S GREAT
12-5
THERE'S A BREAK, VICKI, OLD GIRL! GIVE US A WEEK OR TWO, AND MAYBE WE'LL SHOW THAT DISTRICT ATTORNEY A THING OR TWO
THREE HOURS LATER:
EXTRA! DRINKWATER ARRESTED FOR MURDER!
!
?
12-5
COPR. 1940 BY NEA SERVICE, INC. T. M. REG. U. S. PAT. OFF.

EXTRA!
BLAZES! DRINKWATER ARRESTED FOR MURDER!
BUT—BUT THE DISTRICT ATTORNEY GAVE HIS WORD HE WOULDN'T DO IT
HE LIED! HE DOUBLE-CROSSED US!
THERE MUST BE SOME EXPLANATION, VICKI. COME ON!
12-6
IT'S IMPERATIVE THAT WE SEE THE DISTRICT ATTORNEY AT ONCE
I'M VERY SORRY, BUT MR. LAGEL HAS RESIGNED DUE TO ILL HEALTH
RESIGNED !!!
COPR. 1940 BY NEA SERVICE, INC. T. M. REG. U. S. PAT. OFF.
BUT HE SEEMED IN PERFECT HEALTH THREE HOURS AGO!
MR. LAGEL HAS NOT BEEN FEELING WELL FOR SOME TIME. HE THOUGHT BEST TO GIVE IN TO HIS DOCTOR'S ORDERS

BIRCHFIELD SANITARIUM:
BUT WE'RE NEWSPAPER REPORTERS
WE GOTTA SEE THE DISTRICT ATTORNEY
I TELL YOU, THE DOCTOR HAS GIVEN STRICT ORDERS THAT MR. LAGEL IS TO SEE NO ONE!!
QUIET
12-7
MIGHTY STRANGE, VICKI, THAT THE DISTRICT ATTORNEY'S HEALTH SHOULD GIVE OUT ALL WITHIN THREE HOURS
AND STRANGER STILL THAT HE'D HAVE MR. DRINKWATER ARRESTED JUST AFTER GIVING HIS WORD OF HONOR THAT HE'D WAIT UNTIL OUR INVESTIGATION
12-7
THERE'S ONLY ONE EXPLANATION! COME ON! ONE OF US HAS GOT TO SEE HIM, AND ACCORDING TO MY PLAN, YOU'RE IT
Roy Crane
COPR. 1940 BY NEA SERVICE, INC. T. M. REG. U. S. PAT. OFF.

43

WELL, DRINKY, OLD BOY, YOU'RE IN A FINE MESS! YES SIREE! ALL THE COPS NEED TO SEND YOU TO THE CHAIR IS A MOTIVE FOR WHY YOU KILLED THE GAL
HOW DID YOU GET IN HERE?
AND I GOT THE MOTIVE RIGHT HERE... THIS LETTER. NOW I TELL YOU WOT, PALLY-- I HATE TO SEE A NICE FELLER LIKE YOU GIT A RAW DEAL, SEE?
IF I'M A MIND TO, I KIN DESTROY THIS LETTER AND SAVE YOUR HIDE
WHAT ARE YOUR TERMS?
OH, IT AIN'T MYSELF I'M THINKIN' OF. NO SIREE! IT'S FER THE GOOD OF MY COUNTRY. NATURALLY, YOU'D WANTA RESIGN AS HEAD OF DRINKWATER AIRCRAFT, AND SOMEBODY'S GOTTA SUCCEED YOU. IF I'M GONNA BURN THIS LITTLE LETTER, I'D EXPECT TO NAME YOUR SUCCESSOR
!
!
COPR. 1940 BY NEA SERVICE, INC. T. M. REG. U. S. PAT. OFF.

SO THOSE ARE YOUR TERMS! YOU'LL DESTROY THE LETTER, PROVIDED THAT YOU ARE ALLOWED TO NAME THE NEXT PRESIDENT OF DRINK-WATER AIRCRAFT?
THA'S RIGHT, PALLY. IN A ONE-MAN OUTFIT LIKE YOURS, THERE'S A HEAP COULD GO WRONG UNLESS THE RIGHT MAN STEPS INTO YOUR SHOES
NOW, LIKE AS NOT, WE GOT TH' SAME FELLER IN MIND. WHO'S YOUR CHOICE?
WHY, ROBERTS, OF COURSE. OR HUTTIG, THE CHIEF ENGINEER. BOTH SPLENDID MEN!
NAH, I LIKE THAT LITTLE GUY, WINKLEY, IN TH' SHIPPIN' DEPARTMENT
WHAT! THAT FOOL!
NEVER! I'LL ROT IN JAIL FIRST! I'LL GO TO THE ELECTRIC CHAIR BEFORE I APPOINT A CRACK-BRAINED IMBECILE LIKE WINKLEY
THINK IT OVER, CHUM. THE ELECTRIC CHAIR IS EXACTLY WHERE YOU'LL GO UNLESS HE'S APPOINTED
COPR. 1940 BY NEA SERVICE, INC. T. M. REG. U. S. PAT. OFF.

AH, HA! JUST AS I EXPECTED
EASY'S VIGIL OUTSIDE THE JAIL IS REWARDED
I'M A FEDERAL AGENT, BUDDY. YOU HOLDING YOUR CAB FOR THAT PINK-FACED FELLA?
YEAH. WHY?
HE'S A SABOTAGER. IF YOU CAN KEEP YOUR MOUTH SHUT AND REPORT TO ME WHERE HE GOES, I'LL GIVE YOU $5.
SAY! FOR $5, CAP, YOU CAN EVEN RIDE IN THE TRUNK COMPARTMENT
THEN YOU CAN SEE FOR YOURSELF WHERE HE GOES
SWELL! THIS IS ONE TIME HE WON'T GIVE ME THE SLIP
COPR. 1940 BY NEA SERVICE, INC. T. M. REG. U. S. PAT. OFF.

45

AGAIN MAKING SURE NO ONE IS FOLLOWING HIM, RED, THE BLACKMAILER, SILENTLY UNLOCKS THE DOOR OF A NEIGHBORING BUILDING.
12-19
AND SOON CONCLUDES A REPORT TO HIS "CHIEF"
THIS DRINKWATER'S PATRIOTIC, SEE? HE'S A MAN! WHEN HE SAYS HE'LL GO TO THE 'LECTRIC CHAIR BEFORE NAMING A BOOB AS HEAD OF DRINKWATER AIRCRAFT, HE MEANS IT!
AH, YES, COMRADE. BUT WAIT UNTIL HIS MURDER TRIAL APPROACHES AND WE TURN ON THE REAL PRESSURE — HEH, HEH! HE WILL BE GLAD TO PLAY THE BALL WITH US. YES!
12-19
COPR. 1940 BY NEA SERVICE, INC. T. M. REG. U. S. PAT. OFF.

IT'S A TELEPHONE CALL FROM WILLIE, THE OFFICE BOY, CHIEF! DRINKWATER HAS RESIGNED! THE PRODUCTION MANAGER HAS BEEN NAMED PRESIDENT OF DRINKWATER AIRCRAFT!
!
WHAT!
IT'S JUST LIKE I TOLD YA, CHIEF. DRINKWATER'S PATRIOTIC. HE'S NUTS ABOUT AIRPLANES. HE AIN'T GONNA LET US RUN HIS AFFAIRS, NO MATTER WOT HAPPENS!
?
12-20
SINCE HE HAS NAMED A SUCCESSOR NOT TO OUR LIKING, COMRADES, WE WILL FIND A MEANS OF DESTROYING THE SUCCESSOR, AS WE DID DRINKWATER!
AN ACCIDENT, PERHAPS! A DREAD ILLNESS! OR, EVEN BETTER ...
SHH! SOME ONE IS AT THE DOOR
NOK! NOK!
12-20
COPR. 1940 BY NEA SERVICE, INC. T. M. REG. U. S. PAT. OFF.

THERE'S A DAME AT THE DOOR, CHIEF. A PRETTY BLONDE! THRU THE KEYHOLE I SAW HER
SOON SHE WILL TIRE OF KNOCKING AND GO AWAY
NOW, AS I WAS SAYING, COMRADES, OUR TASK AT DRINKWATER AIRCRAFT IS TO CREATE CONFUSION, DESTROY EFFICIENCY, AND PLAY HAVOC WITH PRODUCTION SCHEDULES
12-21
THIS WE WILL ACCOMPLISH BY DESTROYING ABLE LEADERSHIP. FOR EXAMPLE, ACCORDING TO OUR INDEX CARD, THE NEW PRESIDENT DRIVES AUTOMOBILES 80 MILES AN HOUR. NOW, IF WE CAN ARRANGE AN ACCIDENT...
HELLO! SOME ONE IS AT THE DOOR
NOK! NOK!
IT'S THAT DAME AGAIN, CHIEF
I WILL TOLERATE NO MORE INTERRUPTIONS! OPEN IT, YOU FOOL, AND GET RID OF HER AT ONCE!
12-21
T. M. REG. U. S. PAT. OFF
COPR. 1940 BY NEA SERVICE, INC.

47

EH? THE GIRL WHO TRIED TO SELL US A MAGAZINE SUBSCRIPTION IS MOVING ACROSS THE HALL? LET ME SEE HER
THAT FACE! NEVER DO I FORGET A FACE. WHERE HAVE I SEEN IT BEFORE?
!
12-26
DID YOU HEAR ALL THE WHISPERING AS WE ENTERED THE DOOR, EASY? THEY WERE WATCHING US FROM THE PEEPHOLE
THAT'S TO BE EXPECTED, VICKI
COPR. 1940 BY NEA SERVICE, INC. T. M. REG. U. S. PAT. OFF.
HMM! I WISH I HADN'T LET YOU COME HERE, VICKI. THAT DISGUISE O' YOURS ISN'T GOOD ENOUGH TO FOOL A HIGH-POWERED FOREIGN AGENT WHO'S SEEN YOU BEFORE
I WISH YOU'D STOP WORRYING
12-26
ROY CRANE
BAM!
NOW, I REMEMBER!
NEVER DO I FORGET A FACE! THE GIRL WHO HAS MOVED INTO THE APARTMENT ACROSS THE HALL... SHE IS VICKI!
12-27
VICKI?
VICKI, THE BETRAYER! FROM THE HOUSE FOR CORRECTION. I PICKED HER UP HUNGRY! I GAVE HER WORK! AND SHE BETRAYED US TO THE FEDERAL AGENTS!
COPR. 1940 BY NEA SERVICE, INC. T. M. REG. U. S. PAT. OFF.
OR, MORE LIKELY, SHE WAS A FEDERAL AGENT ALL THE WHILE. YES, THAT IS IT! A FEDERAL AGENT. NOW SHE FOLLOWS ME HERE. COMRADES, WE ARE IN PERIL!
12-27
ROY CRANE
AH, HA! FORTUNATELY THE BACK OF OUR CLOSET IS RIGHT AGAINST THE FOREIGN AGENT'S APARTMENT. BUT BEFORE WE CAN INSTALL ANY LISTENING DEVICE, VICKI, WE'LL NEED A BRACE AND BIT FOR DRILLING PARTLY THRU THE WALL
YOU RUN OVER AND GET IT, EASY, WHILE I GET THE OTHER THINGS IN ORDER
12-28
LOOK, CHIEF -- THE HOOK-NOSED GUY HAS GONE OUT, LEAVIN' THE DAME ALONE
SPLENDID! SPLENDID! OUR OPPORTUNITY, COMRADES, 'AVE ARRIVE!
WOT OPPORTUNITY?
ROY CRANE
12-28 COPR. 1940 BY NEA SERVICE, INC. T. M. REG. U. S. PAT. OFF.
AN OPPORTUNITY TO DESTROY THAT SLY, SLINKING FEMALE G-MAN BEFORE SHE 'AVE DESTROY' US

WHO'S THERE?
IT'S ME, THE JANITOR. I WANTA CONNECT YOUR REFRIGERATOR
BUT... BUT YOU AREN'T THE JANITOR I TALKED TO
OH, AIN'T I?
NICE WORK, NIKOLAS. NOW WE WILL PLACE HER IN THE TRUNK
COPR. 1940 BY NEA SERVICE, INC. T. M. REG. U. S. PAT. OFF.
TO RED'S APARTMENT!
HURRY! NO ONE WILL SEE US IN THE DARKNESS
EVEN SO, THEY WON'T SUSPECT WE GOT A WOMAN IN HERE
NOW, DOWN THE STAIRS AND INTO THE CAR WITH IT!
COPR. 1940 BY NEA SERVICE, INC. T. M. REG. U. S. PAT. OFF.
INTO THE CAR WITH IT, YOU FOOLS! HURRY!
!
BLAZES! FROM VICKI'S DESCRIPTION, THESE ARE THE SABOTEURS!
AND THEY'RE MOVING OUT! I'D BETTER TELL VICKI!
COPR. 1941 BY NEA SERVICE, INC. T. M. REG. U. S. PAT. OFF.
ALAS! LITTLE DOES EASY REALIZE THAT VICKI IS IN THE TRUNK!!

50

51

52

53

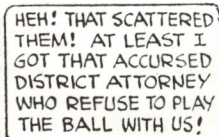

54

55

LET'S FIGURE THIS THING OUT. VICKI WAS KIDNAPED AND BROUGHT TO THIS HOUSE, YET SHE IS NOWHERE TO BE FOUND. A LATCH AND TWO HINGES FOUND IN THE FURNACE ARE OUR ONLY CLUES
1-23
THE TYPE OF LATCH IS USED ONLY ON CLOSET DOORS. AND THE PRESENCE OF NAILS INDICATES THE REST OF THE DOOR WAS BURNED. NOW WHY WOULD ANYONE BURN ONE O' THEIR CLOSET DOORS ?
BUT ALL THE CLOSETS HAVE DOORS
ALL THAT WE'VE SEEN, YES. THEN LET'S LOOK FOR ONE THAT'S BEEN CONCEALED ... AND ITS DOOR BURNED TO DESTROY THE EVIDENCE OF ITS EXISTENCE!
COPR. 1940 BY NEA SERVICE, INC. T. M. REG. U. S. PAT. OFF.
1-23
AH, HA! WET CEMENT!
WET CEMENT! QUICK, GET ME A CROWBAR, OR A CHISEL— ANYTHING!
1-24
THEY HAVE SEALED A CLOSET! HEY, VICKI! VICKI, ARE YOU ALL RIGHT?
JUMPING BLUE BLAZES! SHE'S....
DEAD?
DON'T KNOW YET! GIVE ME A HAND, LIEUTENANT. GET HER INTO THE FRESH AIR
1-24
COPR. 1941 BY NEA SERVICE, INC. T. M. REG. U. S. PAT. OFF.
SHE'S SUFFOCATED. SHE'S NOT DEAD! SHE CAN'T BE!
VICKI! VICKI! SPEAK TO ME!
THAT'S IT! TRY ARTIFICIAL RESPIRATION!
1-25
SHE'S GASPING.. SHE'S TRYING TO MOVE! ATTAGIRL, HONEY! NEVER GIVE UP THE SHIP!
OH! OH! IT WAS LIKE A DREAM... I THOUGHT I HEARD.. SOME ONE CALLING ME HONEY
MUST O' BEEN A DREAM, ALL RIGHT. I DIDN'T HEAR ANYTHING LIKE THAT, DID YOU, LIEUTENANT?
HUMPH!
COPR. 1941 BY NEA SERVICE, INC. T. M. REG. U. S. PAT. OFF.
1-25

57

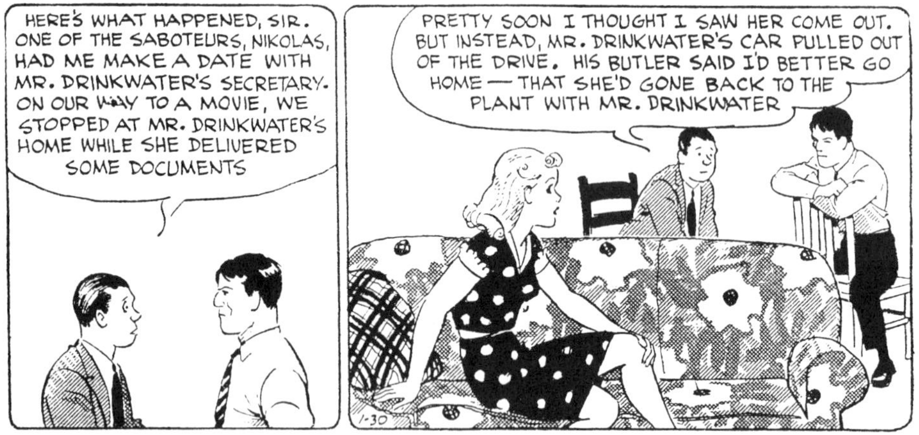

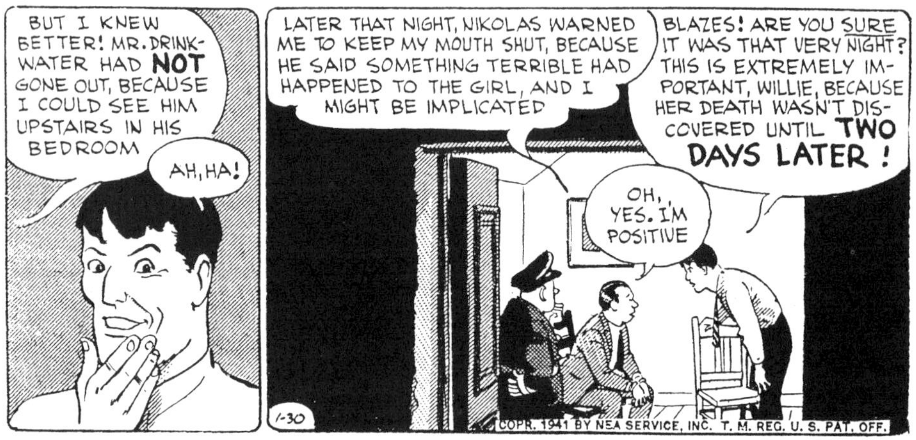

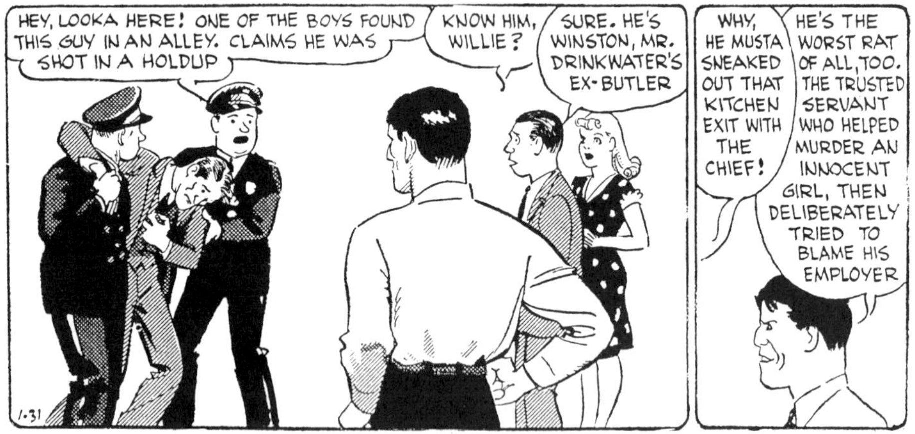

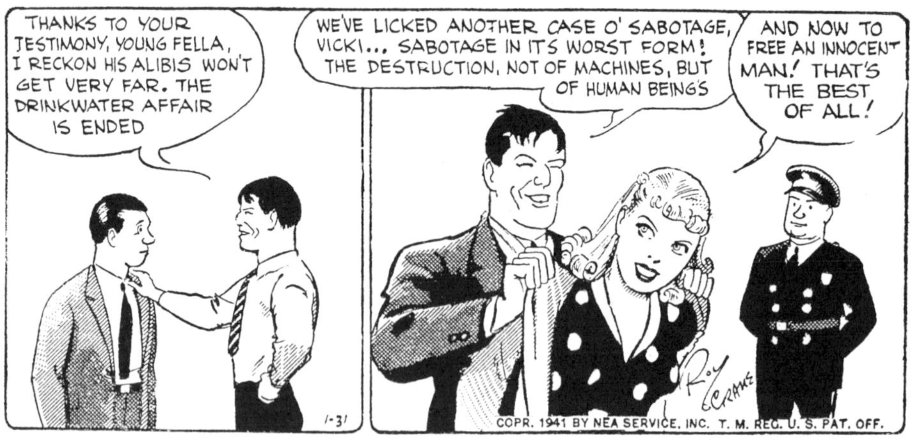

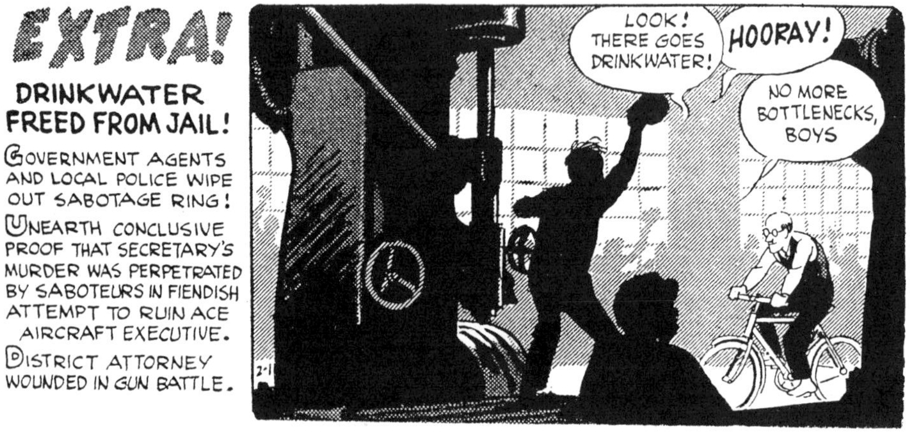

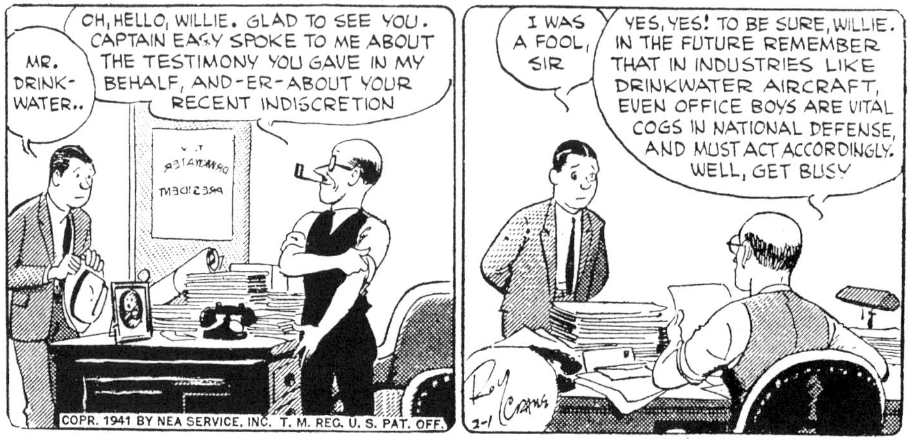

February 1941

59

IN THE OUTSKIRTS OF AN EASTERN CITY LIVES THE NOTED EUROPEAN SCIENTIST, DR. BASSILA
THE LABORATORY FLOOR OF HIS HOME ABOUNDS IN RATS—MOST OF THEM DEAD OR DYING—THE RESULT OF DR. BASSILA'S RESEARCH EXPERIMENTS ON TROPICAL FEVERS
YOU DIDN'T SLEEP WELL, DOCTOR?
AGAIN THE SAME NIGHTMARE... THE RATS IN CAGE 23 ARE BREAK LOOSE. THEY RUN THRU CITY AND SPREAD THE PLAGUE! UGH! IS MOS' HORRIBLE!
WELL, IF I HAD MY WAY, I'D DESTROY EVERY RAT AND GERM IN THE PLACE! I'D BURN THE HOUSE DOWN! I'D...
SHH! SOME ONE IS AT THE DOOR
COPR. 1941 BY NEA SERVICE, INC. T. M. REG. U. S. PAT. OFF.
I 'AVE READ OF YOUR MAGNIFICENT MEDICAL RESEARCH IN THE OLD COUNTRY, DR. BASSILA. MY BROTHER IS MOS' ILL OF THE MALTA FEVER. THE DOCTORS CAN DO LITTLE.
IN DESPERATION I 'AVE COME TO YOU
PLEASE!
I DO RESEARCH WORK IN MEDICINE, YES. BUT A PRACTICING PHYSICIAN, NO!
BUT PERHAPS YOU KNOW OF SOME CURE WHICH HAS NOT YET BECOME KNOWN TO THE MEDICAL PROFESSION AT LARGE?
I 'AVE CONDUC' MANY EXPERIMENTS WIS ANIMALS, YES. SOME WIS PROMISING RESULTS
COPR. 1941 BY NEA SERVICE, INC. T. M. REG. U. S. PAT. OFF.
BOT A SAFE, POSITIVE CURE FOR THE HUMAN BEING — AH, NO! I FEAR IT DO NOT EXIS'
AH!
BARON HAUGCOLRA, ACE OF SABOTEURS, GIVES A SMUG GRUNT OF SATISFACTION
ANOTHER QUESTION, DR. BASSILA: MY SICK BROTHER 'AVE AN ENEMY. CAN IT BE POSSIBLE THIS ENEMY DELIBERATELY TRANSMIT TO MY BROTHER THE GERM OF THE MALTA FEVER?
POSSIBLE, MY DEAR SIR. BOT HIGHLY IMPROBABLE. OH, YES
IN MY EXPERIMENTAL LABORATORY, FOR EXAMPLE, ARE CAGE AFTER CAGE OF POOR, SICK ANIMALS. EACH, IF PERMIT TO GO FREE, CAPABLE OF STARTING AN EPIDEMIC
!
AND HERE... HUNDREDS OF BOTTLES... WHICH CONTAIN CULTURE OF SUCH INFECTIOUS DISEASES AS CHINESE RIVER FEVER, MALTA FEVER, CHOLERA, TYPHUS, DENGUE, TULAREMIA, AND BUBONIC PLAGUE. BOT ONLY A FIEND WOULD DREAM OF INFLICTING THEM ON MANKIND, SIR! ONLY A FIEND!
AH, YES
COPR. 1941 BY NEA SERVICE, INC. T. M. REG. U. S. PAT. OFF.

A HANDSOME LAD! IS THIS YOUR SON, DR. BASSILA?
MY ONLY SON. HE WAS IN THE OLD COUNTRY TAKING POST GRADUATE WORK. I...I 'AVE NOT HEARD FROM HIM SINCE... SINCE HE WAS PLACE IN A CONCENTRATION CAMP
2-10
WHAT A PITY!
WHEN I THINK OF THE HORRORS MY POOR BOY MUS' BE ENDURING... POSSIBLY SICK... POSSIBLY DEAD... I AM ALMOS' CRAZED WITH ANXIETY
THE REAL REASON FOR COMING TO SEE YOU, DOCTOR, IS THAT I 'AVE A MESSAGE FROM YOUR SON
YOU 'AVE SEEN MY CARL? YOU KNOW HIM? OH, PLEASE! TAL ME! IS HE WELL?
Roy Crane
COPR. 1941 BY NEA SERVICE, INC. T. M. REG. U. S. PAT. OFF.
QUITE WELL AND CHEERFUL, BUT...
BUT WHAT?
I REGRET THAT HE IS TO BE SHOT ON THE MORNING OF FEBRUARY NINETEENTH
!!!!
2-10

IS IT NOT BAD ENOUGH THAT MY SON IS IMPRISON IN A CONCENTRATION CAMP? SURELY THEY WOULD NOT SHOOT HIM! OH, NO! NO! IT IS NOT TRUE! IT CAN'T BE TRUE!
THERE IS NO MISTAKE, DR. BASSILA, I ASSURE YOU
2-11
FOR YOUR SON'S — AH — INDISCRETION IN DISCUSSING POLITICS, HE IS TO BE EXECUTED ON THE NINETEENTH
BUT CARL! MY LITTLE BOY! HE IS ALL I 'AVE! ALL!
HIS MOTHER DIE WHEN HE WAS BORN. IT WAS I WHO NURSE HIM, AND CARE FOR HIM, AND PLAY WITH HIM! TOGETHER WE PLAN HIS CAREER — HIS FUTURE! AND, NOW —
NOW!
Roy Crane
COPR. 1941 BY NEA SERVICE, INC. T. M. REG. U. S. PAT. OFF.
OH, NO! NO! THEY MUS' NOT SHOOT MY BOY! OH, PLEASE! IS THERE NOTHING I CAN DO TO SAFE HIM?
WELL, YES— PROVIDED YOU ARE WILLING TO PAY THE PRICE
2-11

IF IT IS IN YOUR POWER TO SAVE THE LIFE OF MY DEAR CARL... TO FREE HIM FROM THE HORRORS OF A CONCENTRATION CAMP IN EUROPE... THERE IS NO PRICE I WILL NOT PAY! ALL MY WORLDLY GOODS, EVERYTHING, I GIF YOU! I SWEAR IT!
TUT, TUT, MY DEAR DOCTOR! I ASK FOR NOTHING GREAT! MERELY A BOTTLE... THE SMALLEST OF BOTTLES CONTAINING A CULTURE OF THE DISEASE CALL MALTA FEVER
2-12
! ! !
2-12
WAT! BETRAY MY PROFESSION AND GIF TO YOU THE MEANS OF SPREADING DISEASE? NO! NO! RATHER WOULD I SEE MY SON DIE IN AGONY AT MY FEET!
Roy Crane
COPR. 1941 BY NEA SERVICE, INC. T. M. REG. U. S. PAT. OFF.

THINK, DR. BASSILA! IT IS IN MY POWER TO PREVENT YOUR SON'S EXECUTION — TO FREE HIM FROM THE HORRORS OF A EUROPEAN CONCENTRATION CAMP. AND ALL I ASK IN RETURN IS ONE SMALL BOTTLE OF MALTA FEVER CULTURE. ONLY ONE
BOT YOU WOULD USE IT TO MAKE PEOPLE SICK! NO! NO!
YOU DON' REALIZE WAT YOU ASK! I 'AVE DEVOTE MY LIFE TO MEDICAL RESEARCH-TO RIDDING MANKIND OF DISEASE. I CANNOT BE A TRAITOR TO MY PROFESSION AND TO MY ADOPTED COUNTRY
YOU ARE A FOOL, BASSILA! CAN IT BE TRUE THAT YOU WOULD 'AVE YOUR SON... YOUR OWN BOY WHOM YOU NURSED AND REARED AND LOVED... SHOT? MURDERED?
THIS IS INHUMAN! GO AWAY! GIVE ME TIME TO THINK!!
I 'AVE WASTED ENOUGH TIME, BASSILA! MAKE YOUR DECISION NOW! WILL YOU SAVE YOUR STUPID PRINCIPLES, OR YOUR SON?
COPR. 1941 BY NEA SERVICE, INC. T. M. REG. U. S. PAT. OFF.

MAKE UP YOUR MIND, BASSILA! EITHER YOU WILL GIVE TO ME THE MALTA FEVER CULTURE, OR YOUR SON WILL DIE IN A CONCENTRATION CAMP. WHICH SHALL IT BE?
MY BOY.... DON' LET HIM DIE!
AH, THANK YOU, DR. BASSILA. THANK YOU! I KNEW YOU WOULD NOT PERMIT YOUR STUPID PROFES-SIONAL ETHICS TO TRIUMPH!
SUCCESS! SUCCESS!! AND NOW THAT HIS MORAL PRINCIPLES 'AVE BEEN BROKEN ONCE, THEY WILL BREAK AGAIN AND AGAIN! I WILL SECURE ALL THE DISEASE GERMS I WISH!
HA, HA! THIS WILL BE THE MOS' BRILLIANT SABOTAGE WORK OF MY CAREER! IN THE RIGHT PLACES, A FEW BOTTLES OF GERMS COULD WRECK THIS COUNTRY'S ENTIRE DEFENSE PROGRAM

200 INDUSTRIAL LEADERS ARE LEAVING A BANQUET WHERE THEY WERE STIRRED BY SPEECHES ON THE URGENCY OF SPEEDING UP NATIONAL DEFENSE
THAT'LL WAKE 'EM UP, EH, JOE?
YOU BET
HA! LET THEM LAUGH AND PLAN BIG THINGS! LITTLE DO THEY SUSPEC' THEY ARE EACH CARRYING AWAY MILLIONS OF GERMS! SOON THEY WILL BECOME ILL, ONE BY ONE... THEY WILL THINK IT IS CAUSE BY SOMETHING THEY ATE
HA, HA! HOW TRUE! BEFORE ANY WAN SUSPEC' SABOTAGE, THEY WILL BE USELESS TO THEIR FACTORIES, AND I WILL BE FAR AWAY AND SAFE. TRULY, THIS IS THE MOS' MAGNIFI-CENT WORK OF MY CAREER!
COPR. 1941 BY NEA SERVICE, INC. T. M. REG. U. S. PAT. OFF.

MR. T.P. TEABURY IS PRESIDENT OF A SMALL FACTORY ENGAGED IN MANUFACTURING PRECISION PARTS FOR ANTI-AIRCRAFT GUNS. HE FEELS SORTA RUN DOWN TODAY
MAYBE IT'S MY LIVER
2-17
CONFOUND IT! THREE O'CLOCK
THAT NIGHT HE DOESN'T SLEEP WELL
NEXT DAY, HE HAS A HEADACHE, AND PAINS HERE AND THERE
MUST BE GETTING RHEUMATISM
2-17
COPR. 1941 BY NEA SERVICE, INC.
THEN HE GOES TO BED WITH FEVER AND A SORE THROAT
INFLUENZA
T. M. REG. U. S. PAT. OFF.
LIKE MANY OTHER INDUSTRIALISTS WHO ATTENDED A NATIONAL DEFENSE BANQUET RECENTLY, MR. TEABURY IS THE VICTIM OF A DIABOLICAL SABOTAGE PLOT, AND IN THE FIRST STAGES OF MALTA FEVER
I STILL BELIEVE HE HAS INFLUENZA
I'D SAY IT'S A FORM OF SEPTICEMIA
SO FAR THE SYMPTOMS ARE ALSO SIMILAR TO TYPHUS, TYPHOID, DENGUE, AND TULAREMIA
MR. TEABURY'S ILLNESS, LIKE THAT OF OTHER INDUSTRIALISTS WHO ATTENDED THE NATIONAL DEFENSE BANQUET, IS HARD TO DIAGNOSE
A LABORATORY TEST IS MADE
MALTA FEVER
POOR FELLOW! I HOPED IT WOULD BE INFLUENZA
2-18
WITHIN TWO WEEKS, 163 CASES ARE KNOWN, ONE FATAL
THE STRANGE PART, DR. WILSON... ALL OF THEM ARE MEN
YES, AND EXTREMELY PROMINENT MEN
2-18
COPR. 1941 BY NEA SERVICE, INC.
MEANWHILE:
WHAT NEWS HAVE YOU HEARD OF MY SON?
HE'S TO BE RELEASED FROM THE CONCENTRATION CAMP TOMORROW, DR. BASSILA. BUT FIRST I MUS' 'AVE ANOTHER BOTTLE OF THE MALTA FEVER CULTURE. I..AH... SPILLED THE FIRST
T. M. REG. U. S. PAT. OFF.
VICKI! HEY, VICKI!
!
?
LISTEN, SILLY, IT'S ONLY 7:30. OUR DATE'S FOR 8 O'CLOCK
YES, YES, I KNOW! BUT A REPORT JUST CAME IN. "163 MEN STRICKEN ILL AFTER ATTENDING NATIONAL DEFENSE BANQUET." WHAT DOES THAT SOUND LIKE?
2-19
BARON HAUGCOLRA!
EXACTLY! IT'S THE CLUE WE'VE BEEN WAITING FOR!
2-19
CAN YOU DRESS, PACK, AND CATCH A PLANE IN EIGHT MINUTES?
SAY! I'M PRACTICALLY READY NOW!
COPR. 1941 BY NEA SERVICE, INC. T. M. REG. U. S. PAT. OFF.

64

65

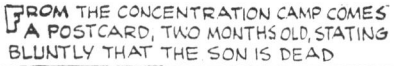

March 1941

66

67

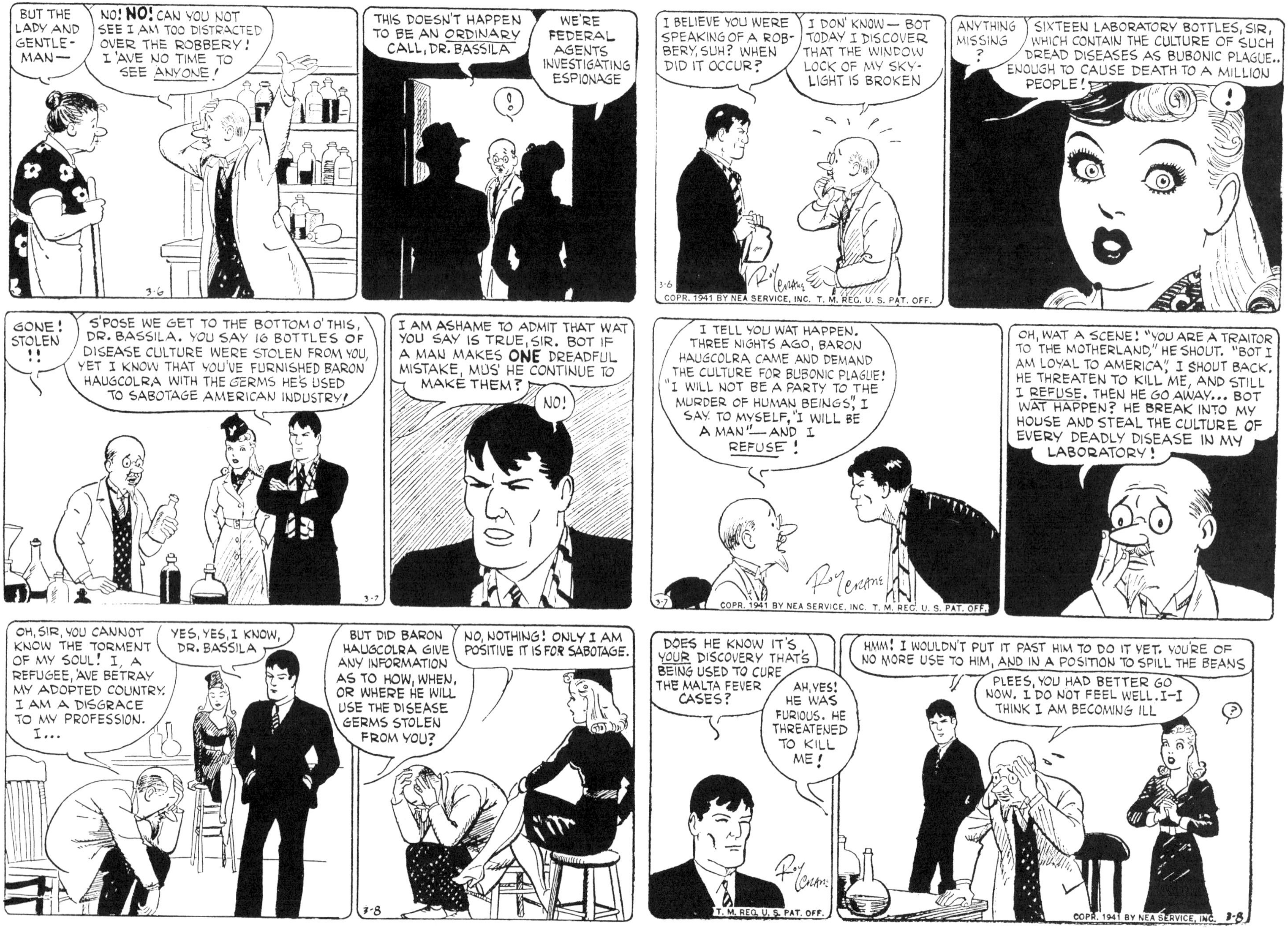
BUT THE LADY AND GENTLE-MAN—
NO! NO! CAN YOU NOT SEE I AM TOO DISTRACTED OVER THE ROBBERY! I 'AVE NO TIME TO SEE ANYONE!
3-6
THIS DOESN'T HAPPEN TO BE AN ORDINARY CALL, DR. BASSILA
WE'RE FEDERAL AGENTS INVESTIGATING ESPIONAGE
!
I BELIEVE YOU WERE SPEAKING OF A ROB-BERY, SUH? WHEN DID IT OCCUR?
I DON' KNOW— BOT TODAY I DISCOVER THAT THE WINDOW LOCK OF MY SKY-LIGHT IS BROKEN
3-6
COPR. 1941 BY NEA SERVICE, INC. T. M. REG. U. S. PAT. OFF.
ANYTHING MISSING ?
SIXTEEN LABORATORY BOTTLES, SIR, WHICH CONTAIN THE CULTURE OF SUCH DREAD DISEASES AS BUBONIC PLAGUE.. ENOUGH TO CAUSE DEATH TO A MILLION PEOPLE!
!
GONE! STOLEN !!
S'POSE WE GET TO THE BOTTOM O' THIS, DR. BASSILA. YOU SAY 16 BOTTLES OF DISEASE CULTURE WERE STOLEN FROM YOU, YET I KNOW THAT YOU'VE FURNISHED BARON HAUGCOLRA WITH THE GERMS HE'S USED TO SABOTAGE AMERICAN INDUSTRY!
3-7
I AM ASHAME TO ADMIT THAT WAT YOU SAY IS TRUE, SIR. BOT IF A MAN MAKES ONE DREADFUL MISTAKE, MUS' HE CONTINUE TO MAKE THEM?
NO!
I TELL YOU WAT HAPPEN. THREE NIGHTS AGO, BARON HAUGCOLRA CAME AND DEMAND THE CULTURE FOR BUBONIC PLAGUE! "I WILL NOT BE A PARTY TO THE MURDER OF HUMAN BEINGS," I SAY TO MYSELF, "I WILL BE A MAN"— AND I REFUSE!
3-7
COPR. 1941 BY NEA SERVICE, INC. T. M. REG. U. S. PAT. OFF.
OH, WAT A SCENE! "YOU ARE A TRAITOR TO THE MOTHERLAND," HE SHOUT. "BOT I AM LOYAL TO AMERICA," I SHOUT BACK. HE THREATEN TO KILL ME, AND STILL I REFUSE. THEN HE GO AWAY... BOT WAT HAPPEN? HE BREAK INTO MY HOUSE AND STEAL THE CULTURE OF EVERY DEADLY DISEASE IN MY LABORATORY!
OH, SIR, YOU CANNOT KNOW THE TORMENT OF MY SOUL! I, A REFUGEE, 'AVE BETRAY MY ADOPTED COUNTRY. I AM A DISGRACE TO MY PROFESSION. I...
YES, YES, I KNOW, DR. BASSILA
BUT DID BARON HAUGCOLRA GIVE ANY INFORMATION AS TO HOW, WHEN, OR WHERE HE WILL USE THE DISEASE GERMS STOLEN FROM YOU?
NO, NOTHING! ONLY I AM POSITIVE IT IS FOR SABOTAGE.
3-8
DOES HE KNOW IT'S YOUR DISCOVERY THAT'S BEING USED TO CURE THE MALTA FEVER CASES?
AH, YES! HE WAS FURIOUS. HE THREATENED TO KILL ME!
T. M. REG. U. S. PAT. OFF.
HMM! I WOULDN'T PUT IT PAST HIM TO DO IT YET. YOU'RE OF NO MORE USE TO HIM, AND IN A POSITION TO SPILL THE BEANS
PLEES, YOU HAD BETTER GO NOW. I DO NOT FEEL WELL. I—I THINK I AM BECOMING ILL
?
COPR. 1941 BY NEA SERVICE, INC. 3-8

69

SURE, I CAN OPERATE A SWITCHBOARD. WHY?
THEN GET BUSY, VICKI. BARON HAUGCOLRA MAY CALL AGAIN AND YOU'D RECOGNIZE HIS VOICE
3-13
SAY, LISTEN HERE...
NEVER MIND THE SQUAWKS, SISTER. WE'RE FEDERAL AGENTS, TRYING TO CATCH THE MOST DANGEROUS SABOTEUR IN THE U.S.A.
SHH! HERE'S A CALL NOW
CITY HOSPITAL? I WISH TO INQUIRE AS TO THE CONDITION OF MY GOOD FRIEND, DR. BASSILA
BLAZES! WHAT LUCK! TELL HIM BASSILA'S BEEN RELEASED FROM THE HOSPITAL AND IS RETURNING HOME
ROY CRANE
3-13
COPR. 1941 BY NEA SERVICE, INC. T. M. REG. U. S. PAT. OFF.

HE'S WHAT?
DR. BASSILA IS FEELING MUCH BETTER AND IS LEAVING THE HOSPITAL
3-14
IT'S IMPOSSIBLE! RIDICULOUS! I, MYSELF, GAVE BASSILA THE GERMS OF A DISEASE FROM WHICH THERE IS SELDOM A RECOVERY... CERTAINLY NOT SO SOON!
YOU KNOW VERY WELL THAT DR. BASSILA'S DANGEROUSLY ILL, EASY. WHY DID YOU HAVE ME SAY THAT?
BECAUSE HAUGCOLRA HAS TRIED TO KILL HIM BY THE TRANSMISSION OF DISEASE
COPR. 1941 BY NEA SERVICE, INC. T. M. REG. U. S. PAT. OFF.
IF HE BELIEVES BASSILA HAS RECOVERED, HE MAY GO TO HIS HOUSE TO LEARN WHAT'S WRONG... POSSIBLY TO COMPLETE THE MURDER. SO I'M GOING TO POSE AS BASSILA, DRIVE TO HIS HOUSE IN AN AMBULANCE, AND AWAIT DEVELOPMENTS
ROY CRANE
3-14

IF YOU'RE GOING TO TRAP HAUGCOLRA, THEN I'M GOING WITH YOU
NO, YOU'D BETTER STAY AT THE HOSPITAL SWITCHBOARD, VICKI, IN CASE HE CALLS AGAIN
3-15
YOU'RE HAVING ME STAY HERE TO BE OUT OF DANGER. I WON'T DO IT!
PLEASE, VICKI, THAT'S NOT THE REASON AT ALL
IT IS! YOU KNOW GOOD AND WELL THAT HAUGCOLRA WON'T GIVE UP WITHOUT A FIGHT. HE'S ARMED! HE'LL SHOOT! HE... HE MAY KILL YOU, EASY!
THEN WISH ME LUCK, OLD TIMER
ROY CRANE
3-15
COPR. 1941 BY NEA SERVICE, INC. T. M. REG. U. S. PAT. OFF.
?
G-GOOD LUCK!
ER... SUPPOSE HE BRINGS A LOT O' MEN WITH HIM, VICKI? HADN'T YOU BETTER WISH ME LUCK AGAINST THEM, TOO?
NO, SILLY. GET OUT OF HERE

71

KINDLY SIT WHERE YOU ARE, BARON HAUGCOLRA, AND RAISE YOUR HANDS SLOWLY
3-20
NOW YOU WILL PLEASE RISE! NO QUICK MOVES, PLEASE
THANK YOU! I SEE YOU TRAVEL WELL ARMED
WHAT IS THIS? WHO ARE YOU?
3-20
CAPTAIN EASY, SUH. SPECIAL AGENT ON SABOTAGE. NO! DON'T MOVE, MY DEAR BARON. I'D BE QUICK TO PULL A TRIGGER ON A ROGUE SO CUNNING AND RUTHLESS AS YOU!
COPR. 1941 BY NEA SERVICE, INC. T. M. REG. U. S. PAT. OFF.
REMOVE EVERYTHING FROM HIS POCKETS, MYRTLE. NO! NOT LIKE THAT! ON YOUR HANDS AND KNEES, AND TO ONE SIDE! THE BARON IS MUCH TOO CUNNING AND DANGEROUS TO TAKE CHANCES WITH!
WITH YOUR PERMISSION, SIR, I WOULD LIKE TO KEEP SUCH PERSONAL EFFECTS AS MY FOUNTAIN PEN AND CIGARET CASE
HMM! LET ME SEE THEM!
3-21
NOT ON YOUR LIFE! THE PEN IS A MINIATURE TEAR GAS GUN, AND THE CIGARET CASE CONTAINS A HIDDEN VIAL. PROBABLY DISEASE CULTURE, EH, BARON?
NO
COPR. 1941 BY NEA SERVICE, INC. T. M. REG. U. S. PAT. OFF.
POISON! IT WAS TO BE USE IN THE EVENT OF MY CAPTURE BY THE POLICE
AH, WELL! TOO BAD, OLD MAN, BUT I'D RATHER SAVE YOU FOR THE ELECTRIC CHAIR. WE HAVE SEVERAL AIR-TIGHT MURDER CHARGES AGAINST YOU
ROY CRANE
3-21
YOU ARE A CUNNING ROGUE, BARON, BUT NOT CUNNING ENOUGH. HAD YOU NOT BEEN SO CURIOUS TO LEARN THE PROGRESS OF DR. BASSILA'S ILLNESS, YOUR PLAN TO SABOTAGE INDUSTRY BY WHOLESALE EPIDEMICS OF DISEASE MIGHT HAVE SUCCEEDED
PERMIT ME TO RETURN THE COMPLIMENT. YOU, TOO, ARE CLEVER
3-22
BUT NOT CLEVER ENOUGH! YOU 'AVE DISCOVER THE VIAL OF POISON I CARRY IN EVENT OF CAPTURE, BUT YOU 'AVE FAIL TO EXAMINE MY COAT LAPEL. PRESTO! I BITE... THEN I SUCK!
HEY, WHAT THE BLAZES!
WITHIN SEVEN MINUTES, POSSIBLY LESS, I SHALL BE DEAD
COPR. 1941 BY NEA SERVICE, INC. T. M. REG. U. S. PAT. OFF.
I 'AVE ... OUTWITTED YOU... AGAIN
3-22
ROY CRANE

73

A SABOTEUR, HEY?
HIS JAW'S BROKEN! WHAT THE HECK DID YOU HIT HIM WITH?
MY FIST
POLIC
3-27
HUMPH! GUYS LIKE HIM ARE LUCKY TO BE ALIVE
THAT NOISE... LIKE A MIGHTY ROAR... CAN IT NOT BE STOPPED?
NOT BY YOU, SUH, NOR BY MEN O' YOUR KIND!
THE NOISE COMES FROM A FACTORY MAKING GUNS FOR THE ARMY AND NAVY!
POLICE
ROY CRANE
T. M. REG. U. S. PAT. OFF.
COPR. 1941 BY NEA SERVICE, INC.
3-27

WE GOT 'IM, VICKI! ANOTHER SABOTAGE CASE IS ENDED! HAUGCOLRA'S BEHIND THE BARS AND THE POLICE ARE RAIDING HIS APARTMENT THIS VERY MINUTE
HOW WONDERFUL!
3-28
WE'RE JUST IN TIME, TOO. THE CHIEF CALLED LONG DISTANCE FROM WASHINGTON. HE WANTS YOU TO CATCH THE FIRST PLANE, WHICH LEAVES IN HALF AN HOUR
WHAT'S UP?
HE WOULDN'T SAY. MUST BE TERRIBLY IMPORTANT. AND BY THE WAY, DR. BASSILA HAS BUBONIC PLAGUE... BUT HE'S EXPECTED TO LIVE
POOR CHAP! HE FEELS THAT HE'S BEEN A TRAITOR ... I'D LIKE TO TELL HIM THAT WITHOUT HIS HELP WE COULD NEVER HAVE CAPTURED HAUGCOLRA
QUIET
I'VE ALREADY TOLD HIM. HE FAIRLY BEAMED WITH PLEASURE. ALSO, I MADE PLANE RESERVATIONS, AND ARRANGED FOR THE HOTEL TO PACK OUR BAGS
VICKI, YOU'RE AN ANGEL! YOU THINK OF EVERYTHING
ROY CRANE
T. M. REG. U. S. PAT. OFF.
COPR. 1941 BY NEA SERVICE, INC.
3-28

WASHINGTON, D.C.
GREAT WORK! SPLENDID! KNEW I COULD DEPEND ON YOU TWO TO RUN DOWN THAT CONFOUNDED HAUGCOLRA! SO HE WAS GOING TO WRECK OUR ARMAMENT PLANTS WITH MICROBES, EH? WHAT A FIEND!
3-29
WHAT'S OUR NEW ASSIGNMENT, CHIEF?
IT MUST BE TERRIBLY IMPORTANT, THE WAY YOU RUSHED US BACK HERE
OH, NO! AS A MATTER OF FACT I WAS GOING TO SUGGEST THAT BOTH OF YOU RUN DOWN TO FLORIDA ON A FISHING TRIP. THE REST'LL DO YOU GOOD
BUT WE DON'T NEED A REST
NONSENSE! NOW RUN ALONG. AND BY THE WAY, EASY, GET A GOOD COAT OF TAN, AND DON'T SHAVE UNTIL FURTHER ORDERS
!
ROY CRANE
3-29
COPR. 1941 BY NEA SERVICE, INC. T. M. REG. U. S. PAT. OFF.
SAY! WHAT THE BLAZES! IS THIS BUSINESS OR PLEASURE?
BOTH. I MAY NEED A DARK, HOOK-NOSED GENT WITH A BEARD.. AND IF SO, I'LL NEED HIM BADLY. WELL, SO LONG

April 1941

AFTER TEN GLORIOUS DAYS ON THE KEYS:
I'M LOOKING FOR A CAPTAIN EASY, SIR
CHIEF!
BLAZES! DON'T YOU KNOW ME?
WELL, BY GEORGE! NO WONDER! WHAT A BEARD! AND BOTH OF YOU AS BROWN AS BERRIES. WONDERFUL!
HEY, BEN! HERE'S THE PHOTOGRAPH. GET TO WORK ON THIS FELLOW
YOU STILL HAVEN'T EXPLAINED WHY YOU HAD ME GROW THIS FACE FULL O' WHISKERS, SUH
THAT WILL COME LATER. IT'S QUITE POSSIBLE THAT A CLEVER DISGUISE WILL PLAY AN IMPORTANT ROLE IN OUR PLANS FOR HEMISPHERE DEFENSE
Roy Crane
COPR. 1941 BY NEA SERVICE, INC. T. M. REG. U. S. PAT. OFF.

OF COURSE, CAPTAIN EASY'S BEARD IS A TRIFLE TOO SHORT TO TRIM, SIR
PERFECT. HIS FOREHEAD'S A BIT TOO LOW, THO. PLUCK HIS HAIR BACK, AND TOUCH UP THE EYE WRINKLES
YES, SIR
THEN GIVE HIM A HAIRCUT, AND DRESS HIM UP, INCLUDING GLASSES
THERE! HE'S A LIVING REPLICA OF THE MAN IN THE PHOTOGRAPH
BY GEORGE! NOT BAD! NOW, EASY, I BELIEVE YOU SPEAK SPANISH. YOU TRAPPED HELGA WOLFE BY USING A SPANISH ACCENT. LET'S HEAR IT
EEF YOU PLEES, SENOR, I WEESH TO KNOW WAT EES THE BEEG IDEA
ROTTEN! TOO MUCH ACCENT! TOO DEEP! WRONG VOICE INFLECTION. GET THE PHONOGRAPH, BEN. PUT ON THE CASTRO RECORDS
Roy Crane
T. M. REG. U. S. PAT. OFF. COPR. 1941 BY NEA SERVICE, INC.

APPARENTLY I'M TO IMPERSONATE SOMEONE WHO SPEAKS SPANISH
THAT'S RIGHT! WE'LL PUT ON A RECORD OF SENOR CASTRO'S VOICE. YOU'RE TO PAY PARTICULAR ATTENTION TO HIS VOICE INFLECTIONS, AND THE WAY HE ROLLS HIS R'S
FOR SEEX YEARS I WAS MEENISTER TO GREAT BRITAIN...
OKAY, EASY
FOR SEEX YEARS I WAS MEENISTER TO GREAT BRITAIN..
WELL, LET'S TAKE OUR COATS OFF. I SEE WHERE THIS IS GOING TO BE A LONG ORDEAL
NOW LISTEN, EASY. YOU'RE NO LONGER A SOLDIER OF FORTUNE. YOU'RE A GENT NAMED MANUEL CASTRO... A POLITICIAN... RICH, SMOOTH, A LADY KILLER. AND YOUR FAT WIFE IS VERY JEALOUS OF BLONDES. OKAY, LET'S TRY IT AGAIN.
!
LET'S SEE IF YOU CAN REALLY ACT
Roy Crane
COPR. 1941 BY NEA SERVICE, INC. T. M. REG. U. S. PAT. OFF.

77

SAN JUAN, PUERTO RICO:
I'M LIEUTENANT RICHARDS, SIR. PLEASE COME WITH ME. I WAS INSTRUCTED TO HAVE A PLANE EQUIPPED WITH A RUBBER BOAT AND FIRST AID KIT, READY TO PUT YOU ABOARD THE S.S. SPLENDORA
4-10
IF YOU'RE READY WE'LL TAKE OFF AT ONCE
I'M READY
GOOD! THIS ASSIGNMENT IS RATHER UNUSUAL. WE DON'T GET 'EM EVERY DAY
NEITHER DO I, SUH
U.S. NAVY
Roy Crane
COPR. 1941 BY NEA SERVICE, INC. T. M. REG. U. S. PAT. OFF.
4-10

THERE'S YOUR STEAMER, BUDDY ... ABOUT EIGHT MILES TO THE SOUTH. IT'LL BE A TICKLISH LANDING, THO, WITH THE SEA AS ROUGH AS IT IS
THEN DON'T RISK IT
4-11
GET WELL AHEAD OF THE SHIP'S PATH, AND I'LL JUMP
HEY! BUT LISTEN...
THANKS A LOT, FELLA
4-11
COPR. 1941 BY NEA SERVICE, INC. T. M. REG. U. S. PAT. OFF.
Roy Crane

THE MAIN THING IS TO LAND IN THE PATH OF THE STEAMER
4-12
SPLASH!
NEXT, TO INFLATE THIS RUBBER BOAT WITH THE BOTTLE OF COMPRESSED AIR—
—AND WRAP BANDAGES AROUND MY HEAD TO HIDE THIS BEARD. A LITTLE MERCUROCHROME TO RESEMBLE BLOOD WILL HELP, TOO. THEN WHEN I'M PICKED UP, IF EVER, I HOPE I'LL PASS FOR THE VICTIM OF A CRASH AT SEA
COPR. 1941 BY NEA SERVICE, INC. T. M. REG. U. S. PAT. OFF. 4-12

A VERY PISTOL BARKS IN THE GROWING DARK
BANG!
DISTRESS SIGNAL, SIR, OFF THE STARB'RD BOW
OH, THE POOR MAN!
ELMER! COME QUICK!
EXCITEDLY, PASSENGERS LINE THE RAIL TO WATCH A RESCUE AT SEA
COPR. 1941 BY NEA SERVICE, INC. T. M. REG. U. S. PAT. OFF.

WHAT HAPPENED?
AN AVIATOR CRASHED AT SEA. THEY'RE RESCUING HIM
OH, HOW THRILLING! I JUST ADORE RESCUES!
TO THE EMERGENCY ROOM, BOYS
SOON AS THEY LEAVE, NELLIE, CLOSE AND BOLT THE DOOR
WELL, YOUNG MAN, THIS IS SEÑOR CASTRO
DELIGHTED! WE WATCH FROM THE PORT-HOLE. YOU WERE MAGNEEFICENT!
COPR. 1941 BY NEA SERVICE, INC. T. M. REG. U. S. PAT. OFF.

TRUE, THERE ARE SPIES ABOARD WHO MIGHT CONCEIVABLY DO ME HARM, AND CERTAINLY CAPITAN EASY HAS COME ABOARD IN A MANNER TO AROUSE NO SUSPICION, BUT TO THINK THAT ANY ONE COULD SUCCESSFULLY IMPERSONATE ME, AH, NO! I FEAR THAT IS ASKING TOO MUCH
WELL, LET'S REMOVE HIS BANDAGES AND SEE
HEAVENS! IT IS LIKE LOOKING INTO A MIRROR!
I 'AVE ALSO MADE AN EFFORT, SENOR CASTRO, TO IMITATE YOUR VOICE AND MANNER OF SPEAKING
GRACIOUS! DOES MY VOICE SOUND LIKE THAT?
NOT QUITE. BUT I'LL BET YOUR CLOSEST FRIENDS WOULDN'T NOTICE THE DIFFERENCE
COPR. 1941 BY NEA SERVICE, INC. T. M. REG. U. S. PAT. OFF.

I AM TO PRETEN' I AM THE INJURED AVIATOR AND REMAIN IN THE SHIP'S HOSPITAL UNTIL WE REACH NUEVO YORK. IS THAT NOT CORRECT, CAPITAN EASY?
CORRECT. AND I'M TO IMPERSONATE YOU, DRAW THE FOREIGN AGENTS OFF YOUR TRAIL, SO YOU CAN PROCEED TO WASHINGTON
BEFORE YOU GO, MI CAPITAN, PLEASE UNDERSTAND THIS IS NOT MY IDEA. I AM NO COWARD. ONLY BECOS YOUR STATE DEPARTMENT INSISTS, DO I PERMIT YOU TO RISK YOUR LIFE FOR ME
I UNDERSTAND PERFECTLY, SUH
ANOTHER THING. I REGRET I CANNOT DESCRIBE TO YOU THE SPIES. BUT THEY ARE ABOARD. AH, YES! AND THEY ARE DANGEROUS. EVEN NOW MY BODYGUARD IS CONFINED TO THIS ROOM WITH A KNIFE WOUND WHICH HE RECEIVE IN COMING TO MY AID LAS' NIGHT
GO TO MY QUARTERS, SUITE 1-A. MY SERVANT IS EXPECTING YOU. HE CAN BE TRUSTED. HAVE NO FEAR THAT ANY ONE WILL SEE THRU YOUR DISGUISE— IT IS EXCELLENT. ADIOS, AMIGO! GOOD LUCK!
COPR. 1941 BY NEA SERVICE, INC. T. M. REG. U. S. PAT. OFF.

I PRESUME YOU ARE PEPE, SENOR CASTRO'S SERVANT?
?
SENOR CASTRO'S SUITE ABOARD THE SPLENDORA!
FOR TEN AND SEVEN YEARS I SERVE THE CASTRO FAMILY AND NOW DON EMANUEL PRETEN' HE DON' RECOGNIZE ME. AH, YES, EET EES THE JOKE. HA, HA!
BOT WAT EES WRONG, DON EMANUEL? WHERE EES THE AMERICANO DETECTIVE WEETH THE BEARD WHO WEEL TAKE YOUR PLACE?
TRULY IT CAN BE SAID THAT I 'AVE PASSED THE ACID TEST, PEPE. I AM THE AMERICANO AND NOT YOUR MASTER
SI, SI! NOW I OBSERVE THE DEEFERENCE...THE EYES... THE VOICE... AH, BOT 'OW AMAZING!
COPR. 1941 BY NEA SERVICE, INC. T. M. REG. U. S. PAT. OFF.

TO THINK, CAPITAN EASY, THAT YOU, AN AMERICANO, BEAR A RESEMBLANCE TO MY MASTER SO AMAZING!
SHH! NOT SO LOUD! WE MAY BE OVERHEARD
NEVER CALL ME EASY. AT ALL TIMES YOU MUS' PRETEN' THAT I AM SENOR CASTRO, UNLESS YOU WISH HIM TO DIE. REMEMBER THAT, PEPE! FOR ME IT IS MOS' DIFFICULT TO PLAY THE PART OF A SOUTH AMERICAN DIPLOMAT. I WILL NEED YOUR HELP AND ADVICE
SI, SENOR
FIRST, WHAT ARE THE HABITS OF SENOR CASTRO?
AT THEES HOUR I DRAW THE BATH, LAY OUT THE CLOTHES FOR DINNER, AND GO TO DINNER MYSELF
GOOD! THAT WE WILL DO AS USUAL. THEN WE MUS' LEARN WHO ARE HIS ENEMIES, FOR IT IS MOS' IMPORTANT TO KNOW WHOM WE ARE TO FEAR AND WATCH
COPR. 1941 BY NEA SERVICE, INC. T. M. REG. U. S. PAT. OFF.

81

EASY'S CAUGHT BY SURPRISE. THERE'S A BRIEF STRUGGLE...THE FLASH OF A KNIFE...
4-24
THEN:
COPR. 1941 BY NEA SERVICE, INC. T. M. REG. U. S. PAT. OFF.
4-24

BLAZES, IT'S LUCKY I ARRANGED FOR THIS CARGO NET TO BE HUNG OVER THE SIDE! WITHOUT BOTH THE NET AND THE BULLET-PROOF VEST I'D BE DONE FOR
4-25
ALL THAT RISK WAS FOR NOTHING, TOO! BECAUSE I STILL DON'T KNOW WHO THE FOREIGN AGENTS ARE WHO TOSSED ME OVER
ONLY ONE THING'S CERTAIN. THEY AREN'T WOMEN. ALL THAT ROUGE AND FEMALE ATTIRE WAS JUST A DISGUISE TO CATCH ME OFF GUARD
T. M. REG. U. S. PAT. OFF.
4-25 COPR. 1941 BY NEA SERVICE, INC.

AFTER THROWING ME OVERBOARD LAST NIGHT, THOSE FOREIGN AGENTS MUST THINK I'M DEAD. VERY WELL, I'LL MAKE THE ROUNDS O' THE SHIP AND WATCH EVERYONE'S EXPRESSION VERY CAREFULLY
4-26
LOOK!
IT'S SENOR CASTRO!
ALIVE! IMPOSSIBLE!
OF ALL THE PEOPLE ON THIS SHIP, ONLY TWO ARE SURPRISED TO SEE ME. I RECKON THAT PROVES WHO THREW ME OVERBOARD
4-26
T. M. REG. U. S. PAT. OFF.
COPR. 1941 BY NEA SERVICE, INC.

83

HERE'S HOW!
ONE MOMENT, PLEASE, AMIGOS. I WISH TO RELATE A LEETLE STORY ABOUT MY FRIEND, THE EMIR OF LATANENGO
ONCE UPON A TIME HE FEARED THAT HIS WICKED BROTHER WAS ATTEMPTING TO STEAL HIS THRONE, SO THE EMIR PLAYED A LEETLE GAME. A MOS' AMUSING GAME. HERE, I WILL SHOW YOU
5-1
HE WOULD TAKE THEIR GLASSES OF WINE, AND QUICKLY... FASTER THAN THE EYE COULD FOLLOW... HE WOULD MOVE THEM ABOUT. BY MISTAKE, THE BROTHER CHOSE THE GLASS INTENDED FOR THE EMIR, DRANK, AND DIED OF HIS OWN POISON!
5-1
BUT, OF COURSE, WE ARE FRIENDS. I WAS MERELY RELATING A LEETLE STORY. AS YOU SAY IN AMERICA, "DOWN THE HATCH!" COME!
?
?
T. M. REG. U. S. PAT. OFF.
COPR. 1941 BY NEA SERVICE, INC.

EXCUSE ME. I... I DON'T THINK I FEEL WELL
ME NEITHER
WAIT! SURELY MY LEETLE GAME OF JUGGLING THE GLASSES OF WINE HAS NOT ALARMED YOU
5-2
OH, NO! IT ISN'T THAT!
YOU INSISTED THAT I DRINK WITH YOU—NOW I AM THE ONE WHO INSISTS. COME! TO OUR HEALTH AND HAPPINESS!
MY HEAD... MY LEGS..
SO, YOU SLINKING RAT, YOU LOADED MY GLASS WITH KNOCK-OUT DROPS, AND GOT THEM YOURSELF!
PROBABLY I WAS RIGHT IN GUESSING THAT THEY ARE THE FOREIGN AGENTS. MEANWHILE, I'LL TAKE THIS OPPORTUNITY OF GOING THRU THIS FELLA'S IDENTIFICATION PAPERS
Roy Crane
COPR. 1941 BY NEA SERVICE, INC. T. M. REG. U. S. PAT. OFF.
5-2

HEY, VICKI! HAD A WIRELESS MESSAGE FROM YOUR SEA-GOING BOY FRIEND THIS MORNING
IS... IS HE ALL RIGHT?
5-3
HAVE THERE BEEN ANY ATTEMPTS TO... TO KILL EASY?
HE MENTIONED ONE OR TWO, I BELIEVE. BUT HE'S FEELING FINE. JUST FINE!
BY THE WAY, YOUNG LADY, AREN'T YOU SHOWING UNMISTAKABLE SIGNS OF FALLING MADLY IN LOVE?
HOW SILLY! OF COURSE I ADMIRE EASY. I THINK HE'S ONE OF THE FINEST, SWEETEST, BRAVEST MEN I EVER KNEW
Roy Crane
T. M. REG. U. S. PAT. OFF. 5-3
YES, YES, I KNOW. ANYWAY, EASY'S LEARNED WHO THE FOREIGN AGENTS ARE. DON'T WORRY ABOUT 'EM. ONE HAS A FORGED PASSPORT, POSSIBLY BOTH. THEY'LL BE ARRESTED THE MOMENT THE SHIP DOCKS
COPR. 1941 BY NEA SERVICE, INC.

85

THERE IS NO EXCUSE FOR INCOMPETENCY OR COWARDICE!
5-8
THEY HAVE DELIBERATELY DISOBEYED MY EXPLICIT INSTRUCTIONS! CASTRO IS STILL ALIVE! FREE!
HIS SHIP DOCKS IN TWENTY MINUTES. WHAT IS THE SHORTEST POSSIBLE TIME IT WILL TAKE TO REACH THERE?
AN HOUR AND A HALF
BUT IS THERE NOT STILL TIME, WHILE HE IS GOING THRU CUSTOMS?
THE LUGGAGE OF A DIPLOMAT, YOU IDIOT, IS NOT SUBJECT TO CUSTOMS EXAMINATION. QUICK! GET ME TO A TELEPHONE. PERHAPS THERE IS STILL TIME TO CALL LUGWIT IN NEW YORK
5-8
COPR. 1941 BY NEA SERVICE, INC. T. M. REG. U. S. PAT. OFF.

NEW YORK. THE SPLENDORA DOCKS
5-9
AH! THERE HE IS!
AND EASY, DISGUISED AS SEÑOR CASTRO, DISEMBARKS
TWO WAITING FOREIGN AGENTS PICK UP HIS TRAIL IMMEDIATELY
FOLLOW THAT CAR!
5-9
T. M. REG. U. S. PAT. OFF.
COPR. 1941 BY NEA SERVICE, INC.

BELIEVING THAT EASY IS SEÑOR CASTRO, THE FOREIGN AGENTS REPORT THAT THEY'VE TRAILED HIM TO A HOTEL
SPLENDID, LUGWIT! SPLENDID! I PERSONALLY WILL BE THERE TO TAKE CHARGE
MEANWHILE, THE REAL CASTRO IS STILL IN THE SHIP'S HOSPITAL WHEN TWO GOVERNMENT AGENTS ARRIVE
IF YOU DON'T MIND, SIR, WE'LL CARRY YOU ASHORE ON A STRETCHER
5-10
JUST A PRECAUTION, YOU KNOW, IN CASE YOU'RE STILL BEING WATCHED
5-10
NO ONE'S FOLLOWING. OKAY, DIXON, WE'LL TAKE HIM STRAIGHT TO THE AIRPORT!
AMBULANCE
T. M. REG. U. S. PAT. OFF.
COPR. 1941 BY NEA SERVICE, INC.

87

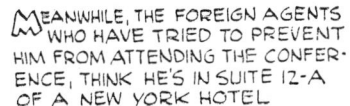

THE SECRET AGENTS SEND FOR A BELLBOY
WE'RE GOING TO A MASQUERADE PARTY, SON. MY FRIEND NEEDS A COSTUME. HERE'S $10 IF YOU'LL LOAN HIM ONE OF YOUR SUITS
SURE
5-15
PUT IT ON, OTTO. THEN TAKE THESE FLOWERS TO THE SUITE OCCUPIED BY SENOR CASTRO. SAY THEY ARE COMPLIMENTS OF THE HOTEL. GET INSIDE, SEE HOW MANY PEOPLE ARE THERE, AND WHAT THE LAYOUT IS
YES, SIR
HA! WITH THE DICTOGRAPH SETUP, WE KNOW EVERYTHING BEFORE IT HAPPENS!
5-15
FLOWERS FOR SENOR CASTRO? SORRY, BUT HE HAS HAY FEVER AND CAN'T STAND THEM
!
COPR. 1941 BY NEA SERVICE, INC. T. M. REG. U. S. PAT. OFF.

I DIDN'T GET INSIDE, WOLFKEG. A MAN IN CASTRO'S SUITE SAID HE HAD HAYFEVER AND COULDN'T STAND FLOWERS
OKAY, THEN WE'LL TRY ANOTHER PLAN
5-16
HMM! SO THE LEADER'S NAME IS WOLFKEG... BY THE WAY, OLD MAN, I EXPECT YOU'RE ANXIOUS TO SEE VICKI. CALL DOWNSTAIRS AND ASK FOR A MANICURIST, AND SHE'LL BE RIGHT UP
12-A
AH, HA! A MANICURIST! THAT GIVES ME AN IDEA
T. M. REG. U. S. PAT. OFF.
COPR. 1941 BY NEA SERVICE, INC.
BOYS, I NEED A MANICURE. LET ME KNOW WHEN THAT KITTEN LEAVES CASTRO. SHE'S GOING TO BE A LOT OF HELP TO US!

WHY, VICKI, OLD PODNER! YOU HAVE A NEW HAIR-DO!
HOW DO YOU LIKE IT?
AHEM! AS I WAS SAYING, WE KNOW EVERYTHING ABOUT THE SABOTEURS IN THE NEXT ROOM AND THEY KNOW NOTHING. FOR ONCE WE HOLD ALL THE CARDS
HUH?
I SAID WE HOLD ALL THE CARDS. OUR PLAN IS WORKING TO PERFECTION. THE SABOTEURS THINK CASTRO'S GETTING A MANICURE... AND THEY WANT A MANICURE NEXT
5-17
THEY'LL CALL VICKI IN AND TRY TO BRIBE HER TO PLAY BALL WITH THEIR SIDE
GOODY, GOODY! I DON'T LIKE EASY'S BEARD... I MAY ACCEPT
BALONEY! YOU'LL KID 'EM ALONG... GIVE THEM A LOT OF MISINFORMATION! WHY, WITHIN 24 HOURS WE'LL HAVE ENOUGH RECORDED EVIDENCE OF EVERYTHING THEY SAY TO PUT THE WHOLE BUNCH BEHIND THE BARS. IT'S A CINCH!
5-17
COPR. 1941 BY NEA SERVICE, INC. T. M. REG. U. S. PAT. OFF.

WHILE A NEAT LITTLE TRAP IS BEING SET FOR THEM, THE CRAFTY SABOTEURS ARE MAKING A ROUTINE SEARCH
HEY! WHAT'S THIS?
THE DISCOVERY IS SHOWN THE CHIEF
A MICROPHONE!!
THE MANICURIST IS LEAVING THE CASTRO SUITE. WANT ME TO STOP HER, CHIEF?
NO. IT'S TIME TO EAT. I'LL GET A MANICURE IN THE MORNING
T. M. REG. U. S. PAT. OFF.
COPR. 1941 BY NEA SERVICE, INC.
It's a trap! Keep talking about food— Destroy all evidence, especially finger-prints. We're clearing out! Hurry!

GUESS THERE'LL BE NO EXCITEMENT TONIGHT, EASY. THE FOREIGN AGENTS ARE GOING OUT TO DINNER. BETTER WARN THE BOYS DOWNSTAIRS TO PICK UP THEIR TRAIL. AND BY THE WAY... I'M GETTING HUNGRY MYSELF. LET'S ORDER A COUPLE OF SWELL DINNERS SENT UP
SURE
PRESENTLY:
ELEVATORS
HEY! WHERE'S THAT GOING?
TO SUITE 12-A, SIR
WELL, WELL! THAT'S CASTRO'S SUITE. DON'T MAKE ANY FUSS, BOYS. JUST TAKE OFF YOUR COATS
!
HA! WE'VE BEEN WANTING TO GET INTO THAT SUITE AND HERE'S OUR CHANCE! LUGWIT, YOU'LL BE THE OTHER WAITER!
COPR. 1941 BY NEA SERVICE, INC. T. M. REG. U. S. PAT. OFF.

THE WELCOME TINKLE OF DINNER DISHES STOPS OUTSIDE THE CASTRO SUITE
HEY, GET OUT OF THE SHOWER, EASY. HERE IT IS
YOU ORDERED DINNER, SIR?
YES, COME RIGHT IN
WHERE WOULD YOU LIKE FOR US TO SET THE TABLE, SIR?
WHY, OVER BY THE WINDOW, I GUESS
COPR. 1941 BY NEA SERVICE, INC. T. M. REG. U. S. PAT. OFF.
THANKS!

HOTEL LOBBY:
EASY PHONED THAT THE FOREIGN AGENTS WERE GOING OUT TO DINNER. YOU KNOW THEIR DESCRIPTIONS. ARE YOU SURE THEY HAVEN'T GONE OUT?
I'M POSITIVE
THAT WAS TWENTY MINUTES AGO. WE MUST HAVE MISSED THEM. BETTER GIVE EASY AND PERKINS A CALL
THAT'S STRANGE! THEY DON'T ANSWER!
GET VICKI AND BURNS AND A PASSKEY! QUICK! SOMETHING MAY HAVE HAPPENED!
HEY, EASY! PERKINS! WHERE ARE YOU?
COPR. 1941 BY NEA SERVICE, INC. T. M. REG. U. S. PAT. OFF.

AGHAST, VICKI AND THE SPECIAL AGENTS SURVEY THE WRECKED "CASTRO" SUITE
PERKINS HAS BEEN BLACKJACKED... EASY'S GONE!
THERE ARE BLOOD-STAINS ON THE BATHROOM FLOOR!!
THE WORK OF THOSE FOREIGN AGENTS— HERE'S WHAT'S LEFT OF THE EVIDENCE PERKINS WAS TAKING
QUICK, VICKI! CALL THE MANAGEMENT... HAVE ALL HOTEL EXITS WATCHED... RUSH ELEVATOR TO THIS FLOOR... NOTIFY F.B.I. GET SOME MEN OVER HERE AT ONCE... COME ON, BOB! WE MAY BE ABLE TO CATCH 'EM BEFORE THEY GET AWAY!
COPR. 1941 BY NEA SERVICE, INC. T. M. REG. U. S. PAT. OFF.

FOREIGN AGENTS BREAK INTO EASY'S SUITE. LEFT BEHIND ARE SIGNS OF A STRUGGLE, BLOODSTAINS, BUT NO EASY!
F.B.I. MEN ARRIVE TO INVESTIGATE
THIS WAS THE THIRD ATTEMPT ON EASY'S LIFE, WASN'T IT, MISS SHERIDAN?
YES
WELL, I GUESS THEY GOT HIM THIS TIME
BUT—BUT MAYBE EASY'S CHASING THEM, OR MERELY KIDNAPED
HUMPH! MORE LIKELY THEY CARRIED HIS BODY OUT. I'LL BET TEN TO ONE HE'S A GONER. TWENTY TO ONE!
HEY! WHAT'S THE MATTER WITH HER?
SHE FAINTED, YOU SAP! SHE'S IN LOVE WITH THE FELLOW
SORRY I TALKED OUT OF TURN, MISS SHERIDAN. MUST HAVE BEEN A DREADFUL SHOCK. PERHAPS YOU'D BETTER LIE DOWN
NO! THIS CASE MEANS A LOT TO ME. I... I'D RATHER KEEP ON WORKING
PLUCKY GIRL!
COPR. 1941 BY NEA SERVICE, INC. T. M. REG. U. S. PAT. OFF.

91

92

LOOK! THERE'S YOUR NAME IN THE PAPER... EMANUEL CASTRO... AND YOUR PICTURE, BOARDING A CLIPPER PLANE FOR SOUTH AMERICA!
MY PICTURE! HOW VER' STRANGE!
DAILY
STRANGE! YOU BET IT'S STRANGE!! YOU'RE S'POSED TO BE IN TWO PLACES AT THE SAME TIME!
AH, HA! WITH CASTRO SAFELY OUT O' THE COUNTRY, I'M NO LONGER OBLIGED TO DOUBLE FOR HIM
6-2
SPEAK, CONFOUND YOU! HOW DO YOU EXPLAIN THAT?
THE EXPLANATION, SUH, APPEARS OBVIOUS
6-2 ROY CRANE
COPR. 1941 BY NEA SERVICE, INC. T. M. REG. U. S. PAT. OFF.
NOT ONCE DID I CLAIM TO BE EMANUEL CASTRO, THO YOU AND YOUR DUMB HOODLUMS ASSUMED THAT I WAS. YOU SPENT YOUR TIME BREAKING INTO HOTEL ROOMS AND BANGING ME OVER THE HEAD WHILE THE REAL AND ONLY CASTRO WAS ATTENDING IMPORTANT AFFAIRS OF STATE. RATHER STUPID, WASN'T IT?

IF YOU'RE NOT EMANUEL CASTRO, THEN WHO THE SAM HILL ARE YOU?
CAPTAIN EASY, SUH, JUST ONE OF THE MANY SPECIAL AGENTS INVESTIGATING YOUR ACTS O' SABOTAGE
6-3
WHY, YOU CONFOUNDED SO AND SO!
WHOP!
SO! YOU'VE MADE A FOOL OF ME!
COPR. 1941 BY NEA SERVICE, INC. T. M. REG. U. S. PAT. OFF.
QUICK, YOU GUYS! WE'VE GRABBED A BLANKETY-BLANKED G-MAN! WE GOT TO GET RID OF HIM!
ROY CRANE
6-3

IF THOSE FOREIGN AGENTS DON'T RELEASE EASY AFTER SEEING THESE NEWSPICTURES OF CASTRO, THEN I'M AFRAID WE'RE SUNK
NONSENSE, VICKI. IMPORTANT CASES ARE OFTEN SOLVED BY INVESTIGATING TRIVIAL CLUES
6-4
BY THE WAY, DOES EASY HAVE A DOG?
NO
NEITHER DOES PERKINS. YET A KEY, TWO BUTTONS, AND A DOG WHISTLE WERE LOST IN THE FIGHT. ALSO, THE VACUUM CLEANER PICKED UP FOUR DOG HAIRS, THREE WHITE AND ONE BLACK, IN THE FOREIGN AGENTS' SUITE
COPR. 1941 BY NEA SERVICE, INC. T. M. REG. U. S. PAT. OFF.
I GET IT. THEN ONE OF THE FOREIGN AGENTS WHO KIDNAPED EASY PROBABLY HAS A BLACK AND WHITE DOG. ALSO HE LIVES OUTSIDE NEW YORK CITY WHERE DOGS RUN LOOSE, OR HE WOULDN'T NEED A WHISTLE
SMART GIRL, VICKI. IT MAY BE THE VERY CLUE WE'RE LOOKING FOR
6-4

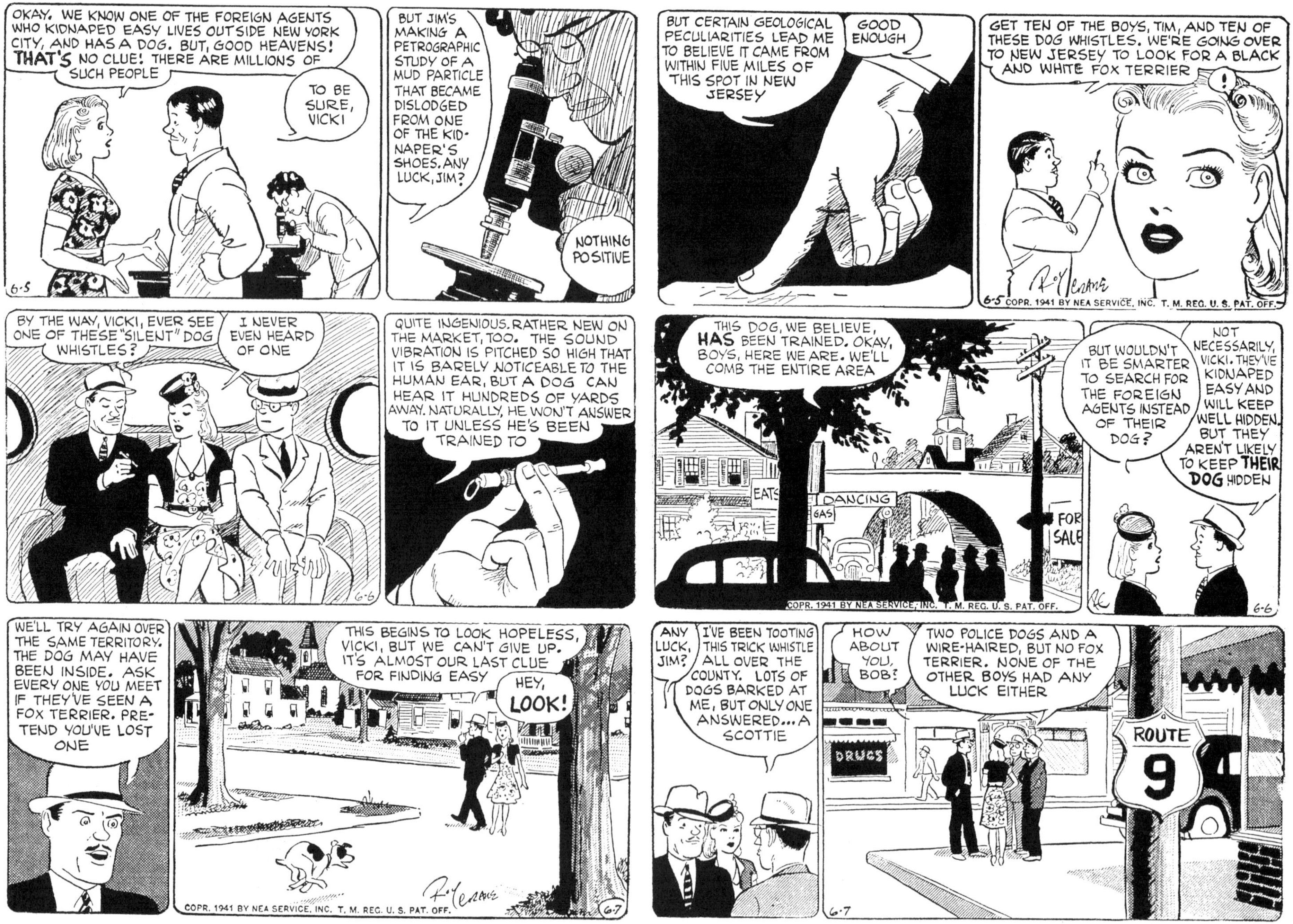
OKAY. WE KNOW ONE OF THE FOREIGN AGENTS WHO KIDNAPED EASY LIVES OUTSIDE NEW YORK CITY, AND HAS A DOG. BUT, GOOD HEAVENS! THAT'S NO CLUE! THERE ARE MILLIONS OF SUCH PEOPLE
TO BE SURE, VICKI
6-5
BUT JIM'S MAKING A PETROGRAPHIC STUDY OF A MUD PARTICLE THAT BECAME DISLODGED FROM ONE OF THE KIDNAPER'S SHOES. ANY LUCK, JIM?
NOTHING POSITIVE
BUT CERTAIN GEOLOGICAL PECULIARITIES LEAD ME TO BELIEVE IT CAME FROM WITHIN FIVE MILES OF THIS SPOT IN NEW JERSEY
GOOD ENOUGH
GET TEN OF THE BOYS, TIM, AND TEN OF THESE DOG WHISTLES. WE'RE GOING OVER TO NEW JERSEY TO LOOK FOR A BLACK AND WHITE FOX TERRIER
!
6-5 COPR. 1941 BY NEA SERVICE, INC. T. M. REG. U. S. PAT. OFF.
BY THE WAY, VICKI, EVER SEE ONE OF THESE "SILENT" DOG WHISTLES?
I NEVER EVEN HEARD OF ONE
6-6
QUITE INGENIOUS. RATHER NEW ON THE MARKET, TOO. THE SOUND VIBRATION IS PITCHED SO HIGH THAT IT IS BARELY NOTICEABLE TO THE HUMAN EAR, BUT A DOG CAN HEAR IT HUNDREDS OF YARDS AWAY. NATURALLY, HE WON'T ANSWER TO IT UNLESS HE'S BEEN TRAINED TO
THIS DOG, WE BELIEVE, HAS BEEN TRAINED. OKAY, BOYS, HERE WE ARE. WE'LL COMB THE ENTIRE AREA
EATS
DANCING
GAS
FOR SALE
COPR. 1941 BY NEA SERVICE, INC. T. M. REG. U. S. PAT. OFF.
BUT WOULDN'T IT BE SMARTER TO SEARCH FOR THE FOREIGN AGENTS INSTEAD OF THEIR DOG?
NOT NECESSARILY, VICKI. THEY'VE KIDNAPED EASY AND WILL KEEP WELL HIDDEN. BUT THEY AREN'T LIKELY TO KEEP THEIR DOG HIDDEN
6-6
WE'LL TRY AGAIN OVER THE SAME TERRITORY. THE DOG MAY HAVE BEEN INSIDE. ASK EVERY ONE YOU MEET IF THEY'VE SEEN A FOX TERRIER. PRETEND YOU'VE LOST ONE
THIS BEGINS TO LOOK HOPELESS, VICKI, BUT WE CAN'T GIVE UP. IT'S ALMOST OUR LAST CLUE FOR FINDING EASY
HEY, LOOK!
COPR. 1941 BY NEA SERVICE, INC. T. M. REG. U. S. PAT. OFF.
6-7
ANY LUCK, JIM?
I'VE BEEN TOOTING THIS TRICK WHISTLE ALL OVER THE COUNTY. LOTS OF DOGS BARKED AT ME, BUT ONLY ONE ANSWERED... A SCOTTIE
HOW ABOUT YOU, BOB?
TWO POLICE DOGS AND A WIRE-HAIRED, BUT NO FOX TERRIER. NONE OF THE OTHER BOYS HAD ANY LUCK EITHER
DRUGS
ROUTE 9
6-7

95

CAREFULLY THE FOREIGN AGENT, LUGWIT, CLOSES THE DOOR BEHIND HIM
HERE IT COMES. HE'S GOING TO BUMP ME OFF
WELL, I'M READY FOR HIM. AT LEAST OLD EASY NEVER GOES DOWN WITHOUT A FIGHT
6-12
BY THE WAY, SON, THE SOUND OF A PISTOL SHOT TRAVELS A MIGHTY LONG WAY ACROSS THE WATER... HADN'T YOU BETTER CLOSE THE WINDOW, TOO?
ER... WELL, MAYBE SO!
6-12
T. M. REG. U. S. PAT. OFF.
COPR. 1941 BY NEA SERVICE, INC.

BAM!
CRASH!
WHAT'S GOING ON IN THERE? HEY, LUGWIT! OPEN THE DOOR!
GREAT SCOTT! LUGWIT'S BEEN KNOCKED OUT!
6-13
WE'LL SHOW THAT BLANKETY-BLANKED G-MAN! GET YOUR GUNS, COMRADES! BREAK THE DOOR DOWN!!
T. M. REG. U. S. PAT. OFF.
6-13
I WOULDN'T TRY THAT IF I WERE YOU. NEXT TIME, I'LL AIM LOWER
?
POW!
COPR. 1941 BY NEA SERVICE, INC.

AND KEEP AWAY FROM THAT WINDOW, TOO!
BANG!
HE'S BARRICADED BEHIND FURNITURE WITH LUGWIT'S GUN. IT'S SO DARK IN THERE, WOLFKEG, WE CAN'T SEE WHERE TO SHOOT
PERHAPS YOU'RE RIGHT, COMRADES
6-14
SURELY, THERE IS A SAFER WAY TO GET RID OF THAT CONFOUNDED G-MAN. BY JINGOES, YES! I HAVE IT!
AN EXPLOSION! GET THE DYNAMITE! THE BARGE IS OF LITTLE VALUE ANY-WAY.... WE'LL DESTROY BOTH TOGETHER!
GASOLINE
COPR. 1941 BY NEA SERVICE, INC. T. M. REG. U. S. PAT. OFF.
6-14

CAPTAIN EASY
by ROY CRANE
SOLDIER OF FORTUNE

August 1940

AND WHAT'S MORE, YOU HORRID, STUPID, LITTLE WORM, I HATE YOU! I DESPISE YOU! FOOEY!
!
YOU AND THE MOVIES—
BAH!
THERE! I'VE DONE IT, EASY—— BUT IT WAS WORTH IT. WILL YOU PLEASE GET ME A TICKET BACK HOME?
SURE, KID. SURE
WAIT! HOLD ON!
THE DIRECTOR THINKS YOU'RE WONDERFUL, MISS DARLING. HE'S NEVER SEEN SUCH EMOTIONAL ABILITY. HE'S GOING TO MAKE YOU A STAR! JUST SIGN ON THE DOTTED LINE, MISS DARLING.
HEY! WATER, SOMEBODY—— SHE'S FAINTED!

102

103

IN PANAMA, 3000 MILES AWAY, IS BEING PLAYED A POKER GAME THAT IS DESTINED TO AFFECT THE CAREERS OF WASH AND EASY.

"I GUESS I GOT YOU **THIS** TIME, RAMON. **FOUR ACES!**"

"SORRY, MY DEAR CAPTAIN—"

"—BUT I HAVE A **STRAIGHT FLUSH!** YOU LOSE AGAIN"

LATER: "SO, YOU DEADBEAT! YOU WELSHER! YOU CAN'T PAY OFF, HEY?"

"PLEASE, RAMON. IF YOU WILL GIVE ME TIME. A YEAR, PERHAPS — OR **TWO** YEARS!"

"GET THIS THRU YOUR THICK SKULL, CAPTAIN LARSEN. YOU'RE GOING TO PAY YOUR DEBT **BEFORE LEAVING THIS PORT.** IS THAT CLEAR?"

"BUT **HOW?**"

"LET ME SEE. YOU'RE CAPTAIN OF THE NELSONS YACHT. THE NELSONS ARE VERY WEALTHY. IN FACT, MISS GINGER NELSON JUST BOUGHT AN UNUSUALLY LARGE DIAMOND FROM THAT WAR REFUGEE, COUNT WAJOSKI."

"SEE HERE! IF YOU EXPECT ME TO STEAL FROM MY EMPLOYERS—"

"NOTHING OF THE KIND, MY DEAR CAPTAIN. A SLIGHT FAVOR IS ALL I ASK. SIMPLY REPLACE YOUR PRESENT CREW WITH SOME OF MY FRIENDS WHO ARE OUT OF WORK, IS ALL."

104

105

106

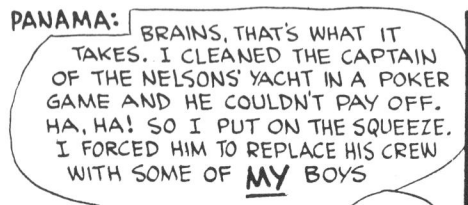

107

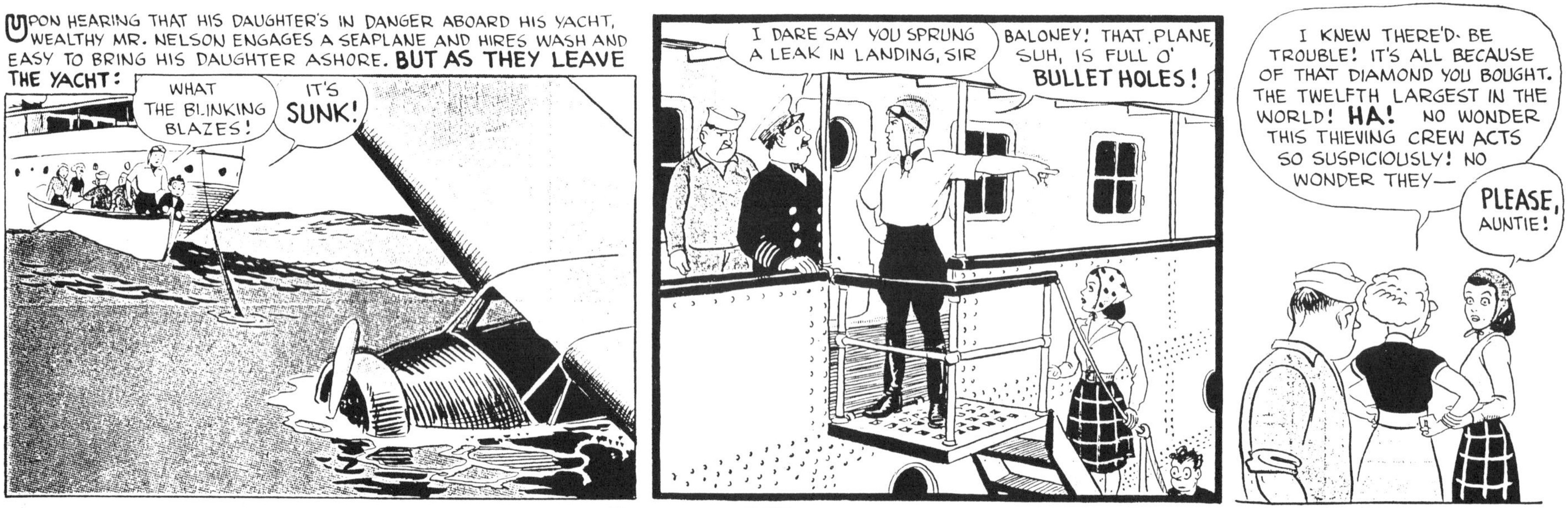

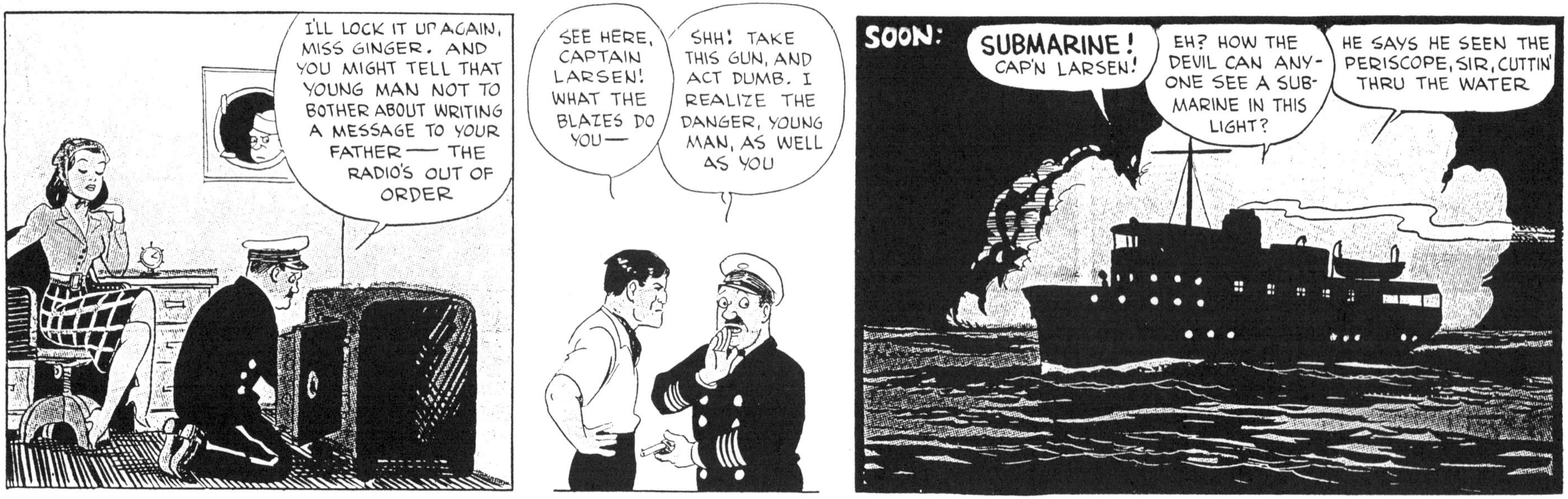

September 1940

109

ABOARD THE YACHT "ADVENTURE" ARE THE TWELFTH LARGEST DIAMOND IN THE WORLD, A CREW OF THUGS, A PRETTY GIRL.
THEN COMES A TERRIFIC EXPLOSION AND DOWN GOES THE "ADVENTURE"
IT HAPPENED SO SUDDENLY
THERE WASN'T EVEN TIME TO GET THE DIAMOND OUT OF THE SAFE
HUMPH! I'LL BET IT WASN'T IN THE SAFE
AT DAWN THEY ARE RELIEVED TO SIGHT A SMALL ISLAND
BUT LOOK! THERE'S THE CREW AHEAD OF US
HA! VERY COMFY! AND PERHAPS SOMEBODY CAN EXPLAIN HOW YOU PACKED YOUR LUGGAGE, LOADED YOUR BOAT AND LAUNCHED IT BEFORE WE HAD TIME EVEN TO REACH THE BOAT DECK?
WODDA YA MEAN, LADY?
I MEAN THIS: YOU WERE ALREADY IN YOUR LIFEBOAT WHEN THE EXPLOSION OCCURRED! YOU STOLE MY NIECE'S DIAMOND, SET OFF A BOMB AND—
AUNTIE!
WHY, YOU MEDDLESOME OLD GOAT, I'LL—
FOR HEAVENS SAKE, AUNTIE, USE YOUR HEAD
OF COURSE WE ALL THINK THAT, MRS. NELSON, BUT WE CAN'T PROVE IT. WE CAN'T EVEN PROVE THAT THE DIAMOND IS MISSING. UNTIL WE CAN, THE LESS SAID THE BETTER
MAROONED WITH A GANG OF PIRATES! BAH!

111

MURDERED! YACHT CAPTAIN FOUND STABBED IN BACK AFTER MYSTERIOUS EXPLOSION SINKS YACHT WITH TWELFTH LARGEST DIAMOND IN WORLD ABOARD
HUMPH! I SUPPOSE THIS THIEVING CREW WILL TRY TO MAKE US BELIEVE THAT A SUBMARINE TORPEDOED HIM, TOO
AUNTIE!
SINCE THERE'S NO ONE ELSE ON THE ISLAND, SUH, IT'S OBVIOUS THAT HE WAS KILLED BY ONE OF US! AND I'D LIKE TO ASK SOME QUESTIONS!
AS FIRST MATE, I'M NOW IN COMMAND HERE, MY YOUNG BUCKO, AND I'LL THANK YOU TO LEAVE THE QUESTIONS TO ME!
LOOK! A BOAT!
QUICK! LIGHT A SIGNAL FIRE

113

SIMPLY BECAUSE I DON'T TRUST ANY MAN ON THIS ISLAND, THAT'S WHY!
AND BESIDES, THEY COULDN'T ANCHOR IN 440 FEET O' WATER! BLAZES! JUST AS I THOUGHT, HE LIED!
DAISY BELLE
COPR. 1940 BY NEA SERVICE, INC.
IT'S ONLY SIXTY FEET DEEP— I'M GOING DOWN FOR A LOOK

115

EXACTLY! IF THAT GUY FINDS OUT THE YACHT IS SUNK IN 60 FEET OF WATER INSTEAD OF 400 — GOOD NIGHT!
OH, MY GOSH! HERE THEY COME!
FIND ANYBODY ABOARD?
NO, BUT THE LADDER'S OVER THE SIDE, AND ONE OF THE DIVING SUITS IS MISSIN'!
DAISY BELLE
HOLY SMOKE!
IT'S THE ONE WITH THE OXYGEN TANK! SOMEBODY'S USING IT! HERE'S THE ROPE HE'LL USE TO COME TO THE SURFACE!
YOU MEAN IT'S THE ROPE HE WAS TO USE
WHOP!
COPR. 1940 BY NEA SERVICE, INC.
SIXTY FEET DOWN:
AT LAST I'VE GOT SOME PROOF ON THOSE BIRDS! THE DIAMOND WAS STOLEN BEFORE THE YACHT EVER SANK! NOW TO GIVE WASH A COUPLE O'JERKS ON THE ROPE AND ....
!
9-22

CAUGHT IN THE ACT OF EXAMINING THE SUNKEN YACHT, EASY'S LIFELINE HAS BEEN CUT BY HIS ENEMIES!
HE FACES ALMOST CERTAIN DEATH SIXTY FEET BELOW THE SURFACE OF THE OCEAN!
OBVIOUSLY, I'VE GOT TO GET OUT O' THE DRINK! BUT HOW?

IF HE'D TAKE OFF HIS LEADEN WEIGHTS, THE AIR IN HIS SUIT WOULD SHOOT HIM TO THE SURFACE!
WELL, WHY THE HECK YOU THINK I'M WAITIN' WITH THIS RIFLE?

LISTEN, BUTCH, AIN'T THINGS IN ENOUGH OF A MESS ALREADY?
THEY AIN'T IN HALF THE MESS THEY'D BE IN IF THAT GUY WAS TO TELL ALL HE KNOWS TO A JURY!
MATE

118

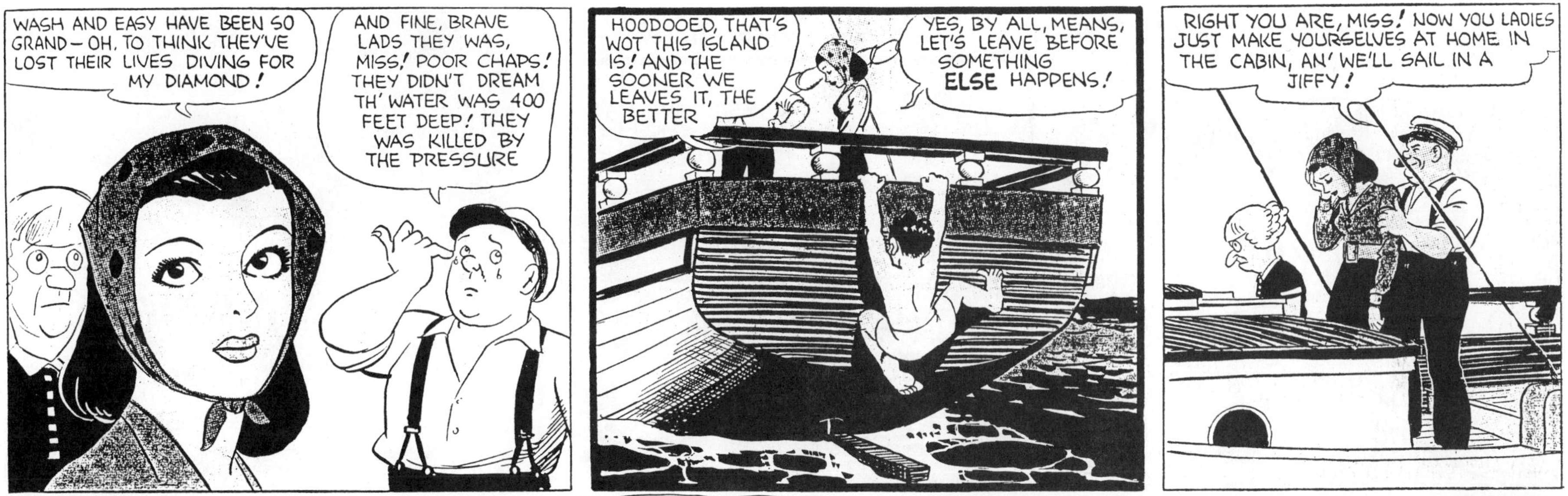

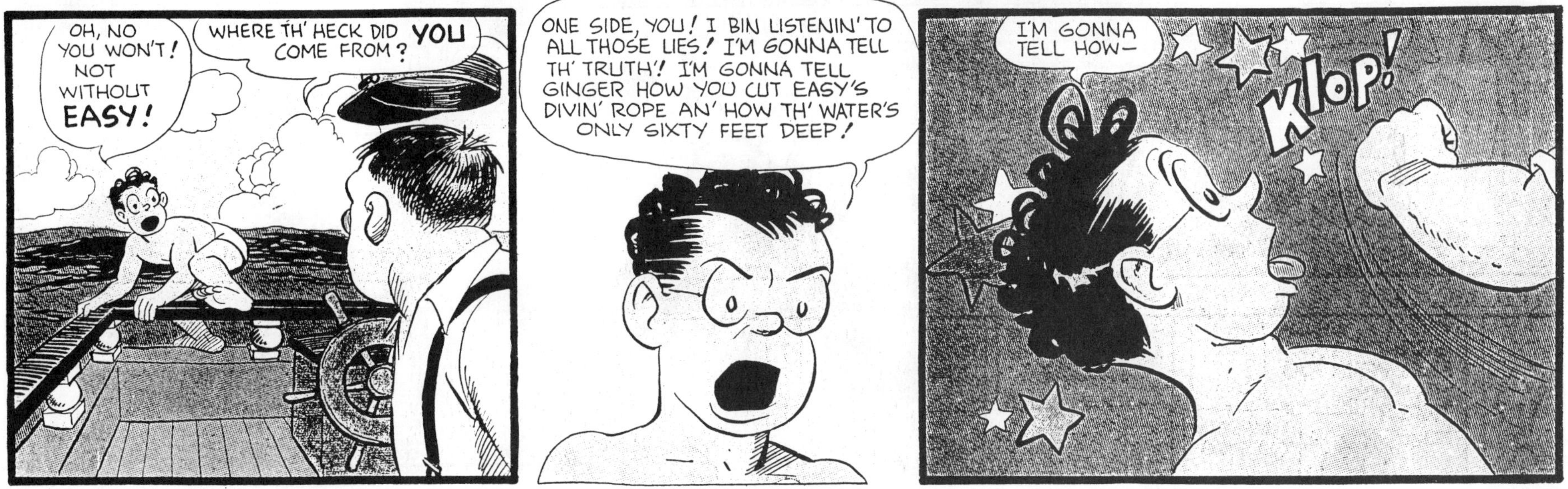

October 1940

HOLD 'IM, SPIKE! KEEP 'IM QUIET! SOON AS THE BOYS COME FROM SHORE WITH THE BOAT, WE'LL MAROON THE BRAT!
THAT'S THE STUFF!
MEANWHILE, EASY IS BY NO MEANS IN A WATERY GRAVE! HE HAS WALKED ASHORE.
NOW TO GET THIS OFF AND PUT ON MY CLOTHES!
HE SENSES THAT THE TIME FOR ACTION HAS COME
HERE'S WHERE BUTCH BURIED IT! IT'S IN A TIN CAN!
I GOT IT!
BLAM!
COPR 1940 BY NEA SERVICE, INC.
10-6
HELP, BUTCH!
THE DIAMOND! HELP!
OUCH!
!

121

122

SAY, JOHN, HOW'D YOU LIKE TO MAKE $5 ?
SURE -- I CAN USE IT FOR COLLEGE NEXT YEAR
HERE'S THE IDEA, SEE? I'VE BEEN KIDDING MY COUSIN FROM THE EAST ABOUT INDIANS. HE THINKS YOU FELLOWS STILL SCALP PEOPLE. NOW YOU PUT ON THIS COSTUME AND TAKE THIS TOMAHAWK
?
THAT'S IT! WALK INTO HIS ROOM AND GIVE A WAR WHOOP
YOWLP!
HAW! HAW! HAW!
I DON'T SEE ANYTHING SO DARNED FUNNY ABOUT THAT! WHO WOULDN'T HAVE BEEN SCARED ?
HO, HO, HAW, HAW! IT'S DAREDEVIL FAUNTLY GILROY! HAW, HAW! THE DARING LIONHUNTER AND DASHING POLO STAR! HE FLEES FROM A HIGH SCHOOL FULLBACK!
OH, IS THAT SO!

WHAT IF I WAS SCARED? LISTEN, YOU LUG, THE MAN DOESN'T LIVE WHO ISN'T AFRAID OF SOMETHING! AND WHAT'S MORE, THERE'S NO MAN ON EARTH WHO WON'T RUN IF HE'S SCARED BY THE RIGHT THING!
BALONEY!
AND JUST TO PROVE IT, I'LL BET MY BEST POLO PONY AGAINST YOUR LAST SUMMER'S STRAW HAT THAT I CAN MAKE ANY MAN IN THIS TOWN RUN AS EASILY!
IT'S A BET! BUT I GET TO CHOOSE THE MAN YOU'RE TO SCARE!
OKAY, CHOOSE ANY MAN YOU LIKE!
THIS IS GOING TO BE A CINCH, FAUNTLY, OLD BOY! TAKE THOSE MINERS, FOR INSTANCE— THEY'RE TOUGH!
AND THOSE COWPUNCHERS. WHY, THEY FACE DANGERS EVERY DAY. NO, WAIT! I'LL PICK THAT FELLOW TALKING TO GINGER NELSON!
THAT GUY? HUMPH!
COPR. 1940 BY NEA SERVICE, INC. T. M. REG. U. S. PAT. OFF.
YOU MAY AS WELL PAY OFF NOW, MY DEAR FAUNTLY! THAT CHAP IS NO OTHER THAN CAPTAIN EASY, SOLDIER OF FORTUNE, ADVENTURER, AND RESCUER OF MY COUSIN GINGER FROM A BAND OF PIRATES! HE CAME BACK TO GET HIS AIRPLANE—UNCLE JOHN SWEARS HE DOESN'T KNOW THE MEANING OF FEAR!
HUMPH! WE'LL SOON SEE ABOUT THAT!
10-20

HIS COURAGE QUESTIONED BECAUSE HE RAN FROM AN INDIAN, FAUNTLY GILROY GETS MAD. HE SAYS THERE'S NOBODY WHO CAN'T BE SCARED. WHAT'S MORE, HE OFFERS TO BET HIS BEST POLO PONY THAT HE CAN CAUSE ANY MAN ON EARTH TO RUN WITH FRIGHT
ALL YOU GOTTA DO IS PICK THE MAN — ANY MAN
OKAY. I'LL PICK EASY
HA, HA! I DARE YOU TO SCARE THAT GUY! WHY, HE HAS MEDALS OF HEROISM FROM ALL OVER THE WORLD! HE'S BRAVED A THOUSAND DEATHS! HE'S FOUGHT EVERYTHING FROM WHALES TO BORNEO HEADHUNTERS! HE'S —
HUMPH! YOU INVITE HIM TO A PICNIC AT UNCLE HENRY'S LODGE TONIGHT. I GUARANTEE HE'LL RUN!
THAT IS, IF YOU PROMISE NOT TO TIP HIM OFF IN ADVANCE
LISTEN, MY DEAR FAUNTLY. I'M SO CONFIDENT YOU CAN'T SCARE EASY THAT I'LL EVEN HELP YOU
EVERYTHING IS ARRANGED
MIGHTY NICE O' THOSE BOYS TO INVITE ME TO THEIR UNCLE'S HUNTING LODGE. I'LL SLICK UP A BIT
I WANT TRAP DOORS AND SECRET PASSAGES GALORE. HIDE BLOOD-STAINED KNIVES AND SKELETONS HERE AND THERE. AND HANG THE EXPENSE! THIS IS A MATTER OF HONOR
FAUNTLY RUNS AROUND TOWN HIRING CARPENTERS AND ELECTRICIANS
ALSO, HE ENGAGES SEVERAL VERY, VERY TOUGH-LOOKING BOZOS
YOU'RE TO WAIT OUTSIDE THE LODGE FOR FURTHER INSTRUCTIONS
SURE

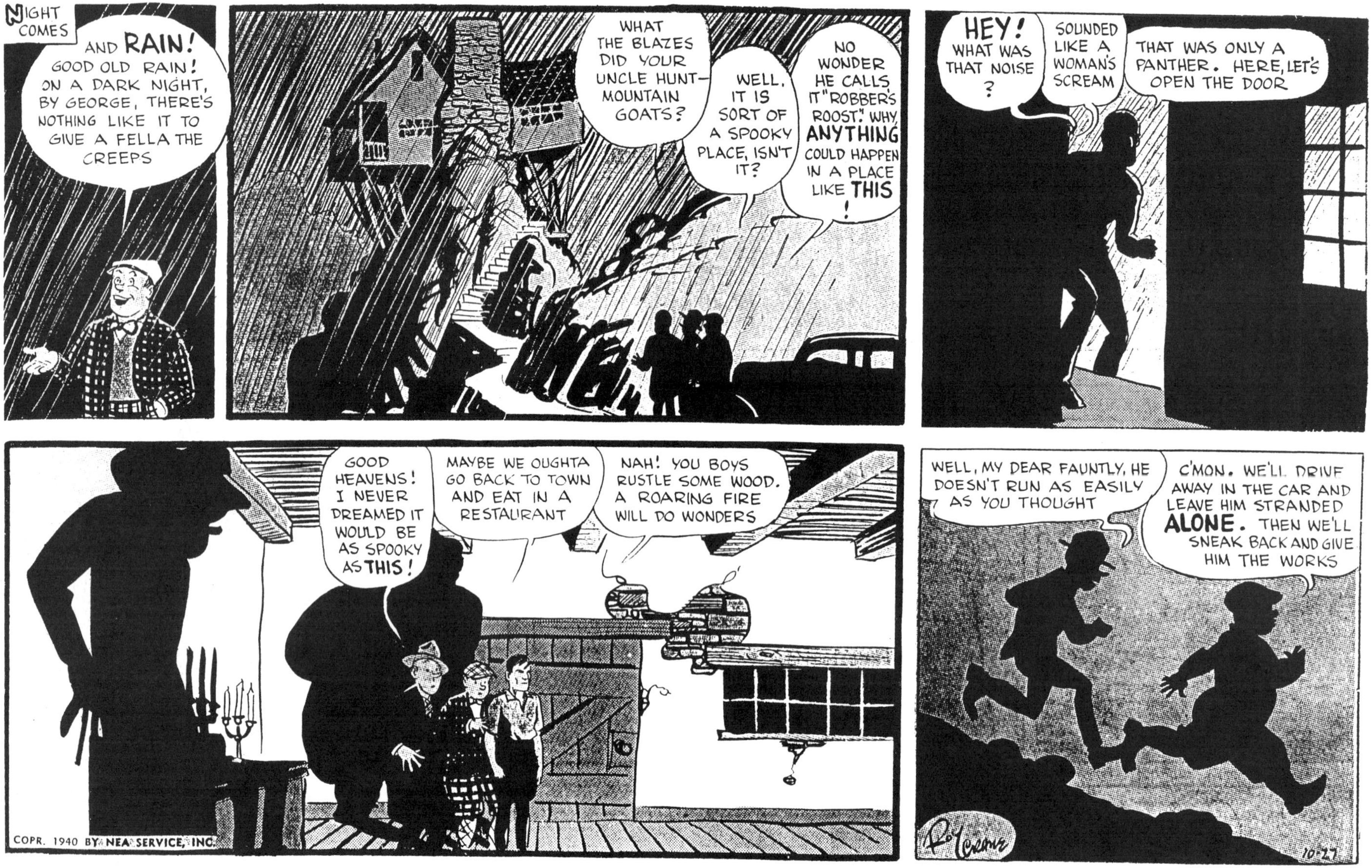
NIGHT COMES
AND RAIN! GOOD OLD RAIN! ON A DARK NIGHT, BY GEORGE, THERE'S NOTHING LIKE IT TO GIVE A FELLA THE CREEPS
WHAT THE BLAZES DID YOUR UNCLE HUNT—MOUNTAIN GOATS?
WELL, IT IS SORT OF A SPOOKY PLACE, ISN'T IT?
NO WONDER HE CALLS IT "ROBBER'S ROOST." WHY, ANYTHING COULD HAPPEN IN A PLACE LIKE THIS!
HEY! WHAT WAS THAT NOISE?
SOUNDED LIKE A WOMAN'S SCREAM
THAT WAS ONLY A PANTHER. HERE, LET'S OPEN THE DOOR
GOOD HEAVENS! I NEVER DREAMED IT WOULD BE AS SPOOKY AS THIS!
MAYBE WE OUGHTA GO BACK TO TOWN AND EAT IN A RESTAURANT
NAH! YOU BOYS RUSTLE SOME WOOD. A ROARING FIRE WILL DO WONDERS
COPR. 1940 BY NEA SERVICE, INC.
WELL, MY DEAR FAUNTLY, HE DOESN'T RUN AS EASILY AS YOU THOUGHT
C'MON. WE'LL DRIVE AWAY IN THE CAR AND LEAVE HIM STRANDED ALONE. THEN WE'LL SNEAK BACK AND GIVE HIM THE WORKS
Roy Crane
10-27

November 1940

128

BETTING HIS BEST POLO PONY THAT HE CAN SCARE THE DAYLIGHTS OUT OF EASY, FAUNTLY GILROY HAS MET WITH FAILURE SO FAR. HOWEVER, HERE COMES ACT NUMBER TWO
JUST WAIT! THERE'S PRACTICALLY NO ONE WHO ISN'T AFRAID OF GHOSTS!
BLAZES! SOUNDS LIKE FOOTSTEPS COMING DOWN THE STAIRS!
?
TAP
TAP
TAP
NOW THEY'RE CROSSING THE ROOM!
DON'T MIND ME, STRANGER. ME AND MY BROTHER ALWAYS COME HERE TO CELEBRATE THE ANNIVERSARY OF OUR ENTRANCE INTO THE SPIRIT WORLD
TAP
TAP
TAP
I SEE
IT WAS 13 YEARS AGO TONIGHT THAT ME AND MY BROTHER WERE MURDERED IN THIS VERY ROOM
AH- WHERE'S YOUR BROTHER?
OH, HE'LL BE ALONG DIRECTLY. PROB'LY HAD A DATE WITH ONE OF THOSE FLIGHTY FEMALE GHOSTS DOWN AT THE CEMETERY, THE OLD SCOUNDREL!
MEANWHILE, A COMPLICATION ARISES. TWO ESCAPED CONVICTS ARRIVE AT THE LONG-DESERTED LODGE
HEY, LOOK! THERE'S A LIGHT IN OUR HIDEOUT!
AND SMOKE'S COMIN' OUTA THE CHIMNEY!

AND THERE'S PEOPLE INSIDE
HEY! MAYBE THEY'RE AFTER THE SWAG WE BURIED IN THE CELLAR! C'MON, LEFTY!
HA, HA! NOW WATCH OLD EASY WHEN THE SECOND GHOST ARRIVES!
SWISH!
WELL, WELL! IF IT ISN'T MY WAYWARD BROTHER!
SEZ YOU! OK., FATTY! FORK OVER THAT WRIST WATCH!
WHO YOU CALLING FATTY? SEE HERE, MY FRIEND —— OW!
THA'S THE WAY, LEFTY! GIVE 'IM A SOCK ON THE BEEZER!
OOF!
CLOP!
UMP!
LICKETY WHOP!
OW!
HELP!
MURDER
POLICE!
HUMPH! A RADIO SPEAKER HIDDEN IN THE CHAIR! I MIGHT O' KNOWN THIS WAS A DIZZY JOKE O' SOME SORT!
COPR. 1940 BY NEA SERVICE, INC.
THE NERVE OF THESE PUNKS, TAKIN' OVER OUR HIDE-OUT! C'MON, LE'S WALLOP THAT GUY UPSTAIRS, TOO!
WAIT. I WANTA SEE WOT THESE ROPES AND GADGETS ARE FOR
SKA-WEEEEEEEEEE
POW
POW!
ROAR!
SWISH
IF OLD EASY THINKS THIS IS A JOKE, FROM NOW ON HE'S MISTAKEN!
Roy Crane

NO LONGER A JOKE! WHEN REAL BANDITS ARRIVE AND BEGIN BEATING UP FAUNTLY GILROY AND HIS COUSIN, FAUNTLY'S WAGER THAT HE CAN SCARE EASY IS FORGOTTEN
KA-PLUMP!
THEN THE BANDITS START ON EASY, DROPPING HIM THRU A TRAP DOOR
WHAT! YOU TIED UP AGAIN?
BANDITS! THEY HAVE GUNS! THEY'VE TAKEN FAUNTLY'S WATCH AND—
I'LL SAY WE DID!
OKAY, SOUR-PUSS! LE'S SEE IF YOU GOT A WATCH, TOO
REACH FER THE SKY! YOU, LEFTY, DIG UP THE BOOTY WE BURIED AFTER THAT BANK ROB'RY FOUR YEARS AGO, THEN WE'LL BEAT 'IM UP
WUMP!
!
LOOK OUT FOR THE LAMP!
LICKETY SPLAT!

WHERE'S FAUNTLY? AND GIL? OH, MY HEAVENS, THEY MUST STILL BE INSIDE THE HOUSE, TIED UP!
I'LL GO SEE
BUT THE TIMBERS ARE BEGINING TO FALL! YOU'LL BE KILLED!
NEVER MIND! HOLD THIS BANK MONEY. TAKE THIS GUN— IF THESE MUGS GET SMART, USE IT!
WELL, HERE GOES NOTHING
OH, NO YA DON'T. SISTER! FORK OVER THAT DOUGH! WE'RE MAKIN' A GETAWAY!
THERE AIN'T NO TIME TO ARGUE, LEFTY! QUICK! THROW HER IN THE CAR AND WE'LL RUN AWAY WITH HER AN' THE MONEY BOTH!
EEK!
HELP!
MURDER!
JOIN RED CROSS
COPR. 1940 BY NEA SERVICE. INC.
11-17
POLICE! I'M BEING KID-NAPED!!!
ONE NICE THING ABOUT GOING ON A PICNIC WITH YOU BOYS— THERE'S NEVER A DULL MOMENT

133

THAT'S EXACTLY WHAT EASY HAS IN MIND. HE CRAWLS CLOSE TO THE STALLED CAR, AND SETS OFF A CANNON CRACKER
WHAT'S THAT?
SOUNDED LIKE A SHOT!
YEE-HOO! C'MON, SHERIFF, WE GOT 'EM CORNERED!
HOLY SMOKE! A POSSE!
QUICK! RUN FER TH' OPPOSITE SHORE!
AS A KID, I WAS PRETTY GOOD WITH ONE O' THESE THINGS
BANG!
YEOW! I'M WOUNDED!
PING!
BANG
KA-POWPOW
OW!
MY LEG!
OUCH
HELP!
DON'T SHOOT NO MORE, SHERIFF!
FER GOSH SAKES, MERCY!!
LATER:
BY GOSH! HE DID IT! WELL, RODNEY, OLD THING, I GUESS YOU'LL HAVE TO ADMIT THAT EASY'S ONE MAN WHO'S AFRAID OF NOTHING!
SMACK!
HUMPH! SOME FELLAS ARE BRAVE— OTHERS ARE DANGED FOOLS! I'M NOT CONCEDING DEFEAT UNTIL I'VE PUT HIM TO ONE MORE TEST!
COPR. 1940 BY NEA SERVICE, INC.

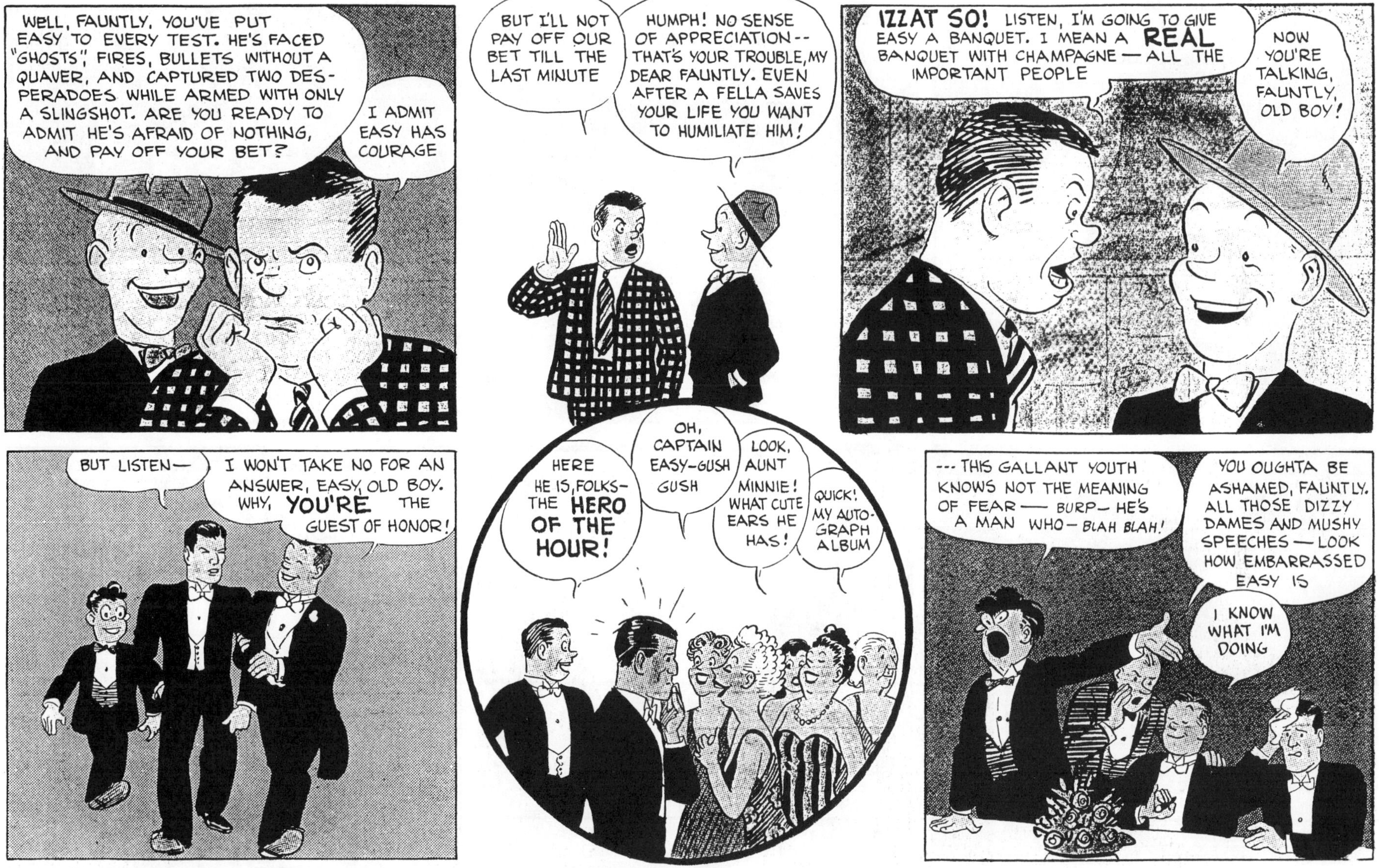

December 1940

136

WHOA! COME BACK HERE, Y'LITTLE RAT!
WHAT HAPPENED ?
THAT SMART ALECK NEWSBOY SNEAKED INTO MY PLACE AND SNITCHED A LIKKER BOTTLE
AW, FORGET IT, MIKE. THE BOTTLE WAS EMPTY
MORNING GLORY BAR
LE'S SCRAM
YA WAS A FOOL, MAXIE. I WARNED YA NOT TO GO IN NO PUBLIC PLACES FOR A DRINK. NOW LOOK WOT HAPPENED
WE CAN GO TO A NEW TOWN
WITH EVERY COP LOOKIN' FOR US, AND THEM SCARS STILL SHOWIN' ON THE NEW FACE THE DOC MADE YOU? NOTHIN' DOIN'! WE GOTTA FIND THE KID AND GET THAT BOTTLE BACK
HEY, MISTER! AREN'T YOU CAPTAIN EASY WHO CAPTURED THOSE ESCAPED CONVICTS WITH ONLY A SLING SHOT?
GUILTY, SON. WHY?
I'M BUDDIE BURNS. I GOTTA SEE YOU ABOUT SUMPIN IMPORTANT. THE COPS WOULD ONLY LAUGH IF I TOLD THEM, BUT YOU WOULDN'T. PLEASE MEET ME IN THE ALLEY IN FIVE MINUTES
WHY, SURE, BUDDIE

138

WE AIN'T GONNA HURT YA, KID, UNLESS YA GET STUBBORN, SEE?
WHERE'S THAT BOTTLE?
OW! MY ARM! YOU'RE BREAKING IT!
OH, YOU'RE THAT CAPTAIN EASY BUDDIE WAS ALWAYS TALKING ABOUT—THE DETECTIVE!
DETECTIVE? ER, MAYBE. ANYWAY, I'M GOING TO TRY TO RESCUE BUDDIE FROM THOSE KID-NAPERS
MY POOR BROTHER! I SIMPLY CAN'T UNDERSTAND WHY ANYONE WOULD WANT TO KIDNAP HIM WHEN WE HAVE SO LITTLE MONEY
BECAUSE HE'S AN AMATEUR SHERLOCK WHO GOT SOME SWELL EVIDENCE. FIRST, WE'LL LOOK FOR THE BOTTLE

AH! SURE ENOUGH! IT WAS HIDDEN IN THE ALLEY WHERE I WAS TO MEET HIM. NOW WE'LL REPLACE THE BOTTLE WITH ANOTHER ONE AND WAIT FOR THE KID-NAPER
SHH! SOME ONE'S COMING!
HA! I FOUND IT!
?
HEAVENS! HE'S GETTING AWAY IN THAT CAR!
THAT'S OKAY, MISS BURNS. FORTUNATELY, THE STREETS AREN'T PAVED—HIS TRACKS WILL BE EASY TO FOLLOW

140

141

STUFF'N NONSENSE, GAL! YOU AIN'T GOT SENSE ENOUGH TO KNOW WHEN YER WELL OFF! HOW MANY TIMES I GOTTER TELL YOU THAT MEN IS A MANGY PACK OF WUTHLESS, LAZY LOAFERS, JEST LIKE YER PAW, WAITIN' FER THE DINNER BELL? GO WASH THE DISHES! AFTER THAT YOU KIN DO THE WASHIN', MILKIN', CHURNIN', WEED THE TURNIPS, AN' MEND THE FENCE
YES'M
THEN COMPLICATIONS AROSE
THEY'S TOO MANY FER ONE HOUSE
I'M TIRED SLEEPIN' FOUR IN A BED
EITHER THE MEN FOLKS HAS GOTTER BUILD AN ADDITION, ER SOMEBUDDY'S GOTTER GIT OUT
WE'LL TAKE A VOTE, BOYS. ALL IN FAVOR OF BUILDIN' AN ADDITION WHICH'LL REQUIRE WORK, SAY "AYE"
NO! NO! NO!
THAT SETTLES IT. WE'LL DRAW STRAWS TO SEE WHO GITS OUT
LULU BELLE LOSES!! SHE'S GOTTER GIT OUT
BUT LULER BELLE! YOU'RE THE ONLY ONE WOT EVER DONE A LICK OF WORK
SHE'S A CAREER WOMAN
SHE KIN SEND US MONEY
COPR. 1940 BY NEA SERVICE, INC
BUT ALL HAS NOT BEEN A BED OF ROSES WITH LULU BELLE. MONTHS HAVE PASSED. UNKNOWN TO WASH AND EASY, SHE'S BROKE AND HUNGRY IN THE VERY TOWN THEY ARE IN
ROY CRANE 12-22

143

I'M JUS' A MISFIT, THA'S ALL. I KIN BITE IRON NAILS IN TWO AN' OUT-WORK ANY MAN ALIVE. BUT I'M TOO FEMININE FER THEM HE-MAN JOBS, THEY SAY, AN' TOO MUSCLE-BOUND FER THE LADY-LIKE STUFF
WE'RE LOOKING FOR WORK OURSELVES
WELL, GLORY BE! I KNOW WHERE WE KIN ALL GIT JOBS, IF YOU KIN GIT US DOWN TO GUATEMALA
EASY HAS AN AIRPLANE
HEY! THEN LOOKIT THIS AD IN YESTERDAY'S PAPER: "BIG MONEY! HELP WANTED IN GOLDEN TROPICS. COOKS, $100 PER MONTH; MECHANICS, $200; TRANSPORT PILOTS, $400. APPLY BIGHEART LAND AND PETROLEUM CO., WAXAJALPA, GUATEMALA"
BLAZES! THAT MIGHT BE WORTH LOOKING INTO
WE'LL WRITE 'EM A LETTER
LETTER ME EYE! GIMME SOME MONEY AN' I'LL SEND A TELEGRAM. LI'L WASHIE KIN BE THE MECHANIC, EASY'LL DO THE FLYIN', AN' I'LL SLING THE HASH. GLORY BE, BOYS! YOU'VE BRUNG ME LUCK!
NEXT DAY:
SOMETHING'S WRONG, LULU BELLE. THEY HAVEN'T ANSWERED YOUR WIRE
HOW MANY TIMES I GOTTER EXPLAIN, YE NINNY? I ONLY AST 'EM TO ANSWER IN CASE THEY DIDN'T WANT US. SO SINCE THEY AIN'T ANSWERED, THEY MUST WANT US. THE JOB'S OURS! LE'S GO!
Roy Crane
12-29
ALL FOR ONE, AN' ONE FER ALL!
SO, AWAY GO THE THREE MUSKETEERS TO FAR OFF GUATEMALA—EIGHT YEARS LATE—TO SEEK THEIR FAME AND FORTUNE.

January 1941

THE BEEGHEART LAND AND PETROLEUM COMPANY? OH, BUT, SEÑORES, THEY DRILL FOR THE OIL AND FIND NOSSING. THEY 'AVE GONE BROKE FI'-SEEX YEARS AGO
MY STARS AN' GULLET! BUT WOT ABOUT OUR JOBS?
YES, THEY ADVERTISED FOR COOKS, MECHANICS, AND PILOTS!
WE SAW THE AD IN A NEWS-PAPER
ALL I KNOW, MY FRANS, EES THE COMPANY SHE EES NO MORE! BROKE, GONE!
BLAZES! LET ME SEE THAT NEWSPAPER AGAIN!
THERE'S THE AD IN BLACK AN' WHITE. YOU KIN SEE FER YERSELF!
JUMPING BLUE BLAZES! NO WONDER! THIS NEWSPAPER, LULU BELLE, IS DATED DECEMBER, 1932, EIGHT YEARS AGO!!
!
COPR. 1941 BY NEA SERVICE, INC.
WELL, GO AHEAD AN' BOOT ME! IT'S ALL MY FAULT
AW, FORGET IT
DON'T TAKE IT SO HARD, LULU BELLE. WE'LL FIND SOME OTHER JOBS. AN' BETTER ONES, TOO, I BETCHA
BUT OUR MONEY'S GONE! OUR GAS IS GONE! WE'RE 2,000 MILES FROM HOME WITH A BUSTED AXLE
MAYBE WE CAN RUN INTO TOWN AN' RUSTLE SOME MONEY
YEAH. WHEN DOES THE NEXT TRAIN LEAVE, BUDDY?
THAT I DO NOT KNOW, SENOR. EET 'AVE NOT RUN IN THE SEEX YEARS SINCE EVER' WAN MOVE AWAY!
1-5

NOT KNOWING THEY WERE AN-SWERING A NEWSPAPER AD EIGHT YEARS OLD, WASH, EASY, AND LULU BELLE FLEW TO FAR OFF GUATEMALA IN SEARCH OF JOBS, ONLY TO FIND THAT THE COMPANY WENT BROKE SIX YEARS AGO.
NOW THEY, TOO, ARE BROKE, AND SO IS THEIR PLANE
DON'T WORRY, LULU BELLE, WE'LL GO TO TOWN AN' MAYBE WE CAN RUSTLE SOME MONEY
IT'S SIXTY MILES THO. THIS GENTLEMAN HAS KINDLY OFFERED US THE USE OF HIS DONKEYS
HE WON'T GO
THAT EES MOS' STRANGE. USUALLY EET EES THE OTHERS WHO WEEL NOT GO
WAIT! I HAVE AN IDEA. LULU BELLE, YOU GET SOME WATER—BARRELS OF IT. WASH, YOU CUT ABOUT THREE CORDS OF WOOD. WHY THE BLAZES SHOULD WE PUSH THOSE DONKEYS INTO TOWN WHEN WE CAN RIDE A TRAIN?
NOW LISTEN, EASY, YOU KNOW DANGED WELL THAT AFTER SETTIN' FER SIX YEARS, THIS OLD TEAPOT AIN'T GUNNER MOVE
UNK!
GAH.
ROAN!
HEY! LISTEN! DID YOU HEAR THAT NOISE? I BELIEVE IT QUIVERED, TOO!
TRY AGAIN
WELL, GLORY BE! IT DONE IT!
WE'RE OFF!
MORE WOOD ON THE FIRE, WASH! WE'RE GOING TO TOWN!
No 1

WUP! CLEAR THE TRACKS!
SUMPIN'S GONNA HAVE TO BE DONE ABOUT THESE BRIDGES, TOO. THEY'RE FULLA TERMITES
FULL SPEED AHEAD, GRIDLEY!
HOT DOG! WE'RE OUTA TH' HILLS!
WHEE!
No. 1
HEY!
Whoa!
WHAT HAPPENED ?
TH' RAILS ARE GONE!
WELL, GLORY TO GOSH! IF'N SOMEBODY AIN'T TORE UP TH' TRACK AS FER AS I KIN SEE! I RECKIN WE'LL HAFTA BORRY THEM DONKEYS AFTER ALL
MEANWHILE:
YOU SAY THEES PLANE BELONG TO A FALLA WHO EES LOOKING FOR WORK?
YES, SENOR. HE EES WITHOUT MONEY AN' MOS' ANXIOUS TO SECURE EMPLOYMENT
THEN MEBBE HE AIN'T SO PARTICULAR AS TO WOT KINDA EMPLOYMENT IT IS. HA! THAT'S FINE! THAT'S SWELL!! WE COULD USE A GUY LIKE THAT, AND HIS PLANE, TOO

149

150

151

YOU WEEL PLEASE NOT REFER TO ME AS "KEEDO"— ONNERSTAND!
ER-YES, MAM
YOU BETCHA!
MORNING:
GOING TO ESTABLISH A NEW BASE OF SUPPLIES, SEE? JUST FOLLOW THESE DIRECTIONS. YOU'RE THE ONLY ONES I CAN TRUST WITH SUCH AN IMPORTANT MISSION
THERE! YA HEAR THAT, SONNY?
THIS IS SEÑORITA TERESA GRANDE, OWNER OF THE NEW BIGHEART LAND AND PETROLEUM CO. A FINE LITTLE LADY, YES, INDEED!
AH!
THEES AVIATOR—SO BEEG AND STRONG! WAT SMOULDERING EYES! I SINK I AM GOING TO LIKE HEEM
I SINK I AM GOING TO LIKE HEEM VER', VER' MUCH! AND I NOTICE HE FOLLOW ME WIS HIS EYES EVER' MOVE I MAKE. THAT EES A GOOD SIGN
ROY CRANE
BOT WHEN HE LEARN THAT I AM TERESA, THE "BUTCHER GIRL", THE MOS' FEARED BANDIT IN ALL CENTRAL AMERICA —— HMM! I WONDAIR EEF HE WEEL LIKE ME THEN?
BY NEA SERVICE, INC.

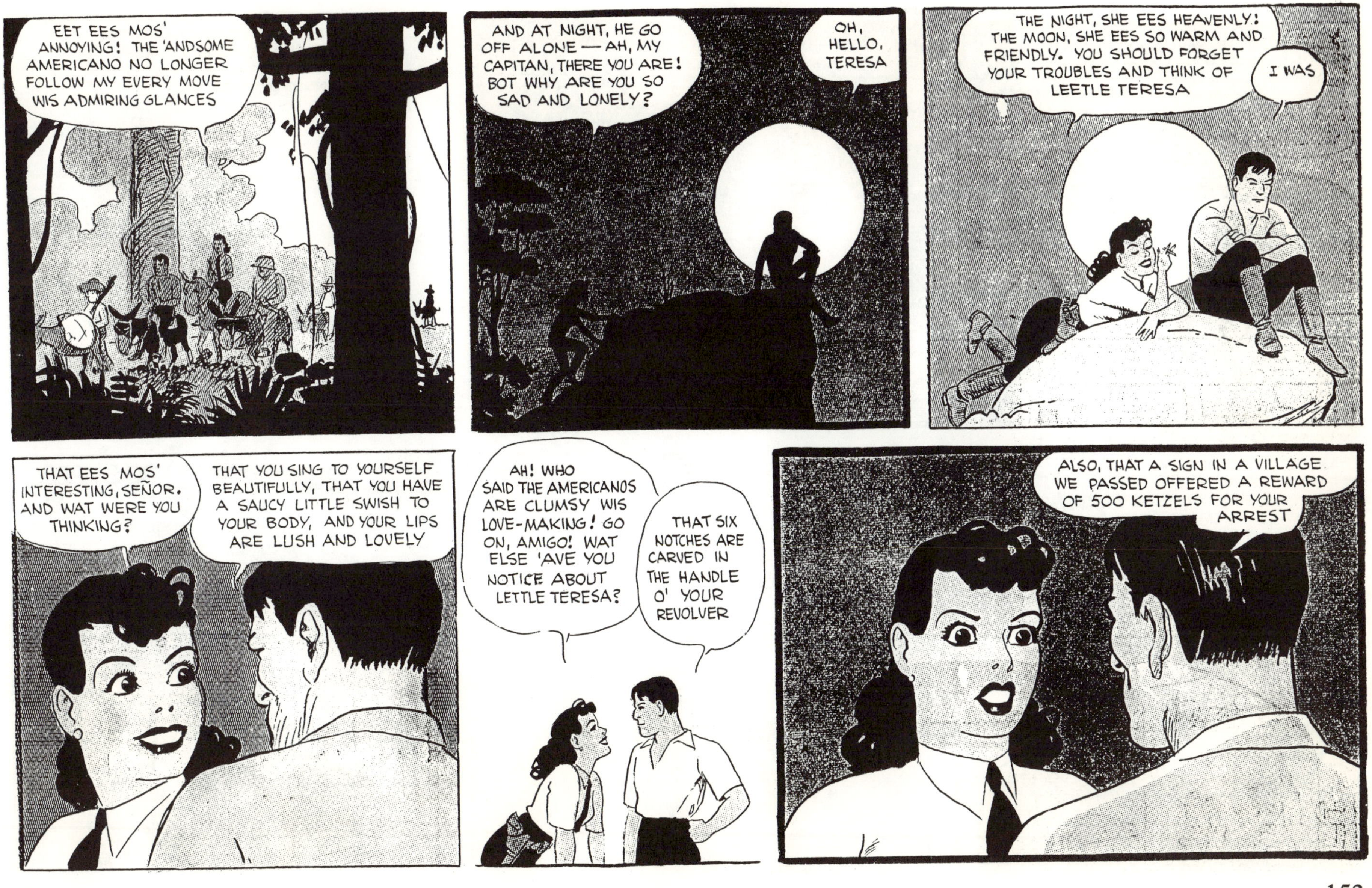

February 1941

YOU 'AVE EYES, MY FRAN, WHICH SEE TOO MUCH! SUPPOSE I AM A BANDIT! SUPPOSE IT IS NOT FOR OIL THAT I AM LOOKING! WAT ARE YOU GOING TO DO?
DESPITE YOUR THREATENING ATTITUDE WITH THAT GUN, SISTER, I'M GOING BACK TO MY FRIENDS
NO, NO! OH, WHY MUS' YOU QUARREL WHEN THE NIGHT SHE EES SO WANDERFUL? STAY! I WEEL SING FOR YOU A GUATEMALAN LOVE SONG
NO!
PLEASE! LET US FORGET OUR QUARREL AND START OVER. WAT WAS IT YOU SAY ABOUT MY FIGURE?
SAUCY AND CUTE
AH, YES! AND MY EYES—MY LIPS! LOOK AT THEM, EASY. LOOK CLOSELY! AND TAKE ME INTO YOUR ARMS BEFORE YOU GO
SURE
FORTUNATELY, ANGEL, I DON'T CLOSE MY EYES WHEN I KISS—I WAS WATCHING
DOG! PEEG OF A MAN! YOU 'AVE LIPS OF FIRE, BOT A HEAD OF ICE! I HATE YOU!
2-2
COPR. 1941 BY NEA SERVICE, INC

SO! WHILE KISSING A MAN, YOU'D STAB HIM IN THE BACK!
OKAY, BEEG BOY, WAT ARE YOU GOING TO DO ABOUT EET, HEY?
I'M GOING TO TIE YOU TO THIS TREE, MY LITTLE WILDCAT, AND RETURN TO MY FRIENDS, AS I TOLD YOU. IF ANYTHING'S HAPPENED TO THEM, I'LL WRING YOUR PRETTY NECK, TOO!
YOU WEEL PLEASE TO RAISE THE HANDS ABOVE THE HEAD, SEÑOR
SANK YOU, GABRIEL! THEES PEEG-HEADED FOOL— HATE HEEM!!
BUENO, SEÑORITA! THEN I WEEL SHOOT HEEM LIKE A DOG
NO!
WHAT'S THE IDEA, TERESA? YOU TURNING SISSY?
PERHAPS, AFTER THE TENDER EMBRACE OF THE GRINGO PILOT, THE DREAD "BUTCHER GIRL"— THE TERROR OF GUATEMALA— EES EEN LOVE AGAIN, YAS?

156

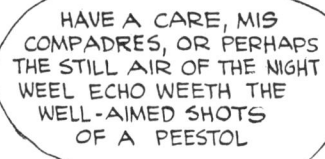

157

OUR HEARTS ARE OPEN TO YOU, ORPHAN SINGER
ON THE MORROW THERE WILL BE A FEAST IN YOUR HONOR
YOU WILL DRINK FROM THE SACRED GOBLET OF MAYAN KINGS, AND SLEEP ON A ROBE OF HUMMING BIRD FEATHERS
THEN YOU WILL SING FOR US IN THE GOLDEN VOICE AND TELL OF YOUR TRAVELS BEYOND THE SEAS
THEES MY PEOPLE—MY HOME! I LOVE THEM! EEF YOU DARE TELL THAT TERESA EES BANDIT, I KEEL YOU LIKE A DOG!
WAITED A LONG TIME FOR A VISIT, EH, LITTLE PRIMA DONNA?
AND WHY? BECOS I WAS ASHAME TO RETURN AND TELL THE TRUTH! BECOS I WAS BETRAY BY THAT DOG OF A MAESTRO AND FORCE TO WORK EEN A CHEAP DANCE HALL! BECOS WAN TIME HE CHOKE ME SO HARD I LOSE THE GOLDEN VOICE AND CAN NO LONGER HOPE TO SEENG LIKE THE BIRDS
I—I'M SORRY, TERESA. I DIDN'T UNDERSTAND
AH, HOW MAGNIFICENT! EVEN THE GRINGO BELIEVE YOU ARE HOMESICK
BUT HOW ABOUT ALL THESE RELATIVES AND—?
AFTER 12 YEARS, POOF! I AM HARD AS NAILS! TO ME THEY ARE NOSSING!
I WEEL ASK TO PRAY EEN THE HIDDEN TEMPLE WHERE EVEN TODAY ARE WORSHIPPED THE PAGAN GODS. I WEEL DEESCOUVER WHERE ARE HIDING THE ANCIENT ORNAMENTS OF GOLD AND ONYX THAT THE BEEG MUSEUMS OF CHICAGO AND NUEVO YORK SO MUCH WANT
BUENO!
LEAVE IT TO TERESA! SHE'LL GET 'EM, TOO

IN THE VILLAGE WHERE SHE WAS BORN, TERESA IS KNOWN AS THE "GIRL OF THE GOLDEN VOICE WHO WOULD SING BEFORE EMPERORS ACROSS THE SEAS." THEY DON'T KNOW THAT SHE HAS BECOME TERESA, "THE BUTCHER GIRL," MOST FEARED BANDIT IN GUATEMALA
WE MUST DO HONOR TO OUR ILLUSTRIOUS GUEST
AT THE FEAST SHE WILL SING FOR US
YOU WILL SLEEP ON A ROBE OF HUMMING BIRD FEATHERS, LITTLE SISTER
AND DRINK FROM THE ANCIENT GOBLET OF MAYAN KINGS
MADRE DE DIOS! IT'S GOLD!
WHY, A MUSEUM WOULD PAY THOUSANDS OF DOLLARS FOR THIS STUFF
POOF! YOU 'AVE SEEN NOSSING
COME WIS ME
AS A CHILD I REMEMBER. BEYOND THAT SENTRY EES WHERE ARE KEPT MANY RELICS SUCH AS ARE POSSESS BY NO MUSEUM ON EARTH

Panel 1: EVEN BEFORE THE SPANISH CONQUISTADORES, THEES WAN BEEG HOLY PLACE. THE VOLCANO, EET DESTROY THE TEMPLE AND THE HOUSES. EET KEEL MANY PEOPLE AND RUIN THE CROPS. BUT THE PEOPLE WEEL NOT LEAVE, EVEN EEF THEY STARVE, OR DIE, BECOS OF THE SACRED RELICS

Panel 2: HA, HA! THE RELICS WON'T BE HERE LONG, EH, TERESA?

NOT AFTER MEEDNIGHT. AH, 'OW FORTUNATE I LEAVE THEES PLACE WHEN LEETLE GIRL! NO LONGER AM I THE FOOLISH INDIAN. I AM HARD! I EAT SENTIMENT—BAH!

SHH! THE GRINGO!

Panel 3: LISTEN, KID, YOU AREN'T NEEDED ANY MORE. SCRAM! GET OUTA TOWN! YOU'RE FIRED!

YES, SUH

Panel 4: BUT EASY DOESN'T GO FAR. INSTEAD, HE AND A NEW PET WAIT IN THE NEARBY JUNGLE

ARE YOU AND I GOING TO SEE THESE POOR INDIANS ROBBED OF THE ONLY WORTHWHILE POSSESSIONS THEY HAVE, TITO? BLAZES, NO!

Panel 5: MEANWHILE:

EASY AND THE OTHERS ARE GONE!

THEN WE'LL FOLLY THEIR TRAIL. THE IDEE OF THAT OIL FELLER SENDIN' US TO THE MIDDLE OF A SWAMP TO WAIT FER HIM! JUST LEAVE ME GIT MY HANDS ON HIM!

Panel 6: Y'BETTER BE CAREFUL, LULU BELLE. THERE MIGHT BE TROUBLE

YOU BETCHER PINK PANTIES THERE'S GUNNER BE TROUBLE! HE'LL WISHT HE NEVER SEEN THE LIKES OF LULU BELLE WALLIS AFORE I'M FINISHED!

TERESA IS WAITING FOR THE HOUR OF MIDNIGHT, WHEN SHE AND HER BANDITS ARE TO SNATCH THE ANCIENT MAYAN TREASURES FROM THE INDIAN VILLAGE WHERE SHE WAS BORN. SHE HEARS A WHISTLE OUTSIDE

OH, EES ONLY YOU!

THE MOON IS BEAUTIFUL, TERESA— I COULDN'T LEAVE WITHOUT SEEING YOU JUST ONCE MORE

AH! BOT I THOUGHT YOU DEED NOT CARE FOR LEETLE TERESA

SOMETIMES I DON'T. THEN AT TIMES YOU SEEM FINE AND— AND SORTA HUMAN INSIDE

TITO

I HAF A MONKEE NAME TITO ONCE. AH, BOT HE WAS NICE! HE SNUGGLE ONDER MY CHIN LIKE THEES WAN, AND I CRY AND CRY WHEN I WENT AWAY AND LEF' HEEM

ANYWAY, LET'S NOT DISCUSS IT. LOOK, I HAVE A PRESENT FOR YOU

A MON-KEE! OH, 'OW DAR-LEENG! WAT EES HEES NAME?

THEN I LIVE WIS MY GRANDMOTHER EEN A HOUSE LIKE THEES— AND THERE WAS A ROCK TO SLIDE DOWN— AND GRANDMOTHER WOULD BE AT THE OVEN COOKING HONEY-CAKES! AH, BOT THEY WERE DELICIOUS!

March 1941

161

I SLEEP EEN A ROOM LIKE THEES. AND EEN THE WINDOW I KEEP MY—MY———
LEESTEN, YOU GRINGO DOG! YOU ARE TOO SMART! THEES MY HOUSE—THEES WHERE I AM BORN! YOU TALK WIS THE INDIANS AND LEARN EVEN THE KIND OF DOLL I 'AVE WHEN LEETLE GIRL! YOU SINK YOU MAKE TERESA, THE BUTCHER GIRL, INTO A SENTIMENTAL SEESY— BOT YOU MEESTAKEN
ALWAYS THE HARD-BOILED BANDIT, EH, TERESA? I RECKON YOU'D THROW YOUR NEW PET DOWN THE WELL.
NO, NO, YOU FOOL! CAN YOU NOT SEE THAT HE TRUS' AN' ADORE ME?
THAT'S WHY I DON'T LIKE YOU AT TIMES, TERESA. YOU'RE DECENT AND TRUE TO A DUMB ANIMAL——YET YOUR OWN PEOPLE, WHO ARE EQUALLY INNOCENT AND TRUSTING, YOU'D ROB, CHEAT, AND BETRAY! YOU'RE IMPOSSIBLE!
THINK IT OVER
OKAY, GRINGO! YOU WIN! PERHAPS—DEEP EENSIDE—I AM NOT SO HARD AS I SINK. I CANNOT BETRAY MY OWN PEOPLE—NO! BOT COME—HURRY! EVEN NOW MY BANDITS ARE MAKING READY TO ROB THEM!
3-2 COPR. 1941 BY NEA SERVICE, INC.

163

WHAT ?
SAY! WOT'S EATIN' YOU? WHY, WE'VE PLANNED THIS HAUL FOR MONTHS!
DO AS I TAL YOU! PUT EET DOWN! GO, GET OUT!
ARE YOU CRAZY?
NOTHIN' DOIN! ME AN' GABRIEL AIN'T GETTIN' OUT EMPTY-HANDED! IF THA'S THE WAY YOU RUN THINGS, THE TIME HAS COME TO ELECT A NEW LEADER!
EES THAT SO?
YES, THA'S SO! YOU AIN'T HARD-BOILED NO MORE, TERESA! SUMPIN'S CHANGED YOU
HA! AND I KNOW WAT 'AVE CAUSE THE CHANGE — SHE'S EEN LOVE WIS THE YANQUI CAPITAN!
AND THEES TAM — CARRAMBA! NO WAN EES GOIN' STOP ME FROM KEELING HEEM!
NO! NO!
KA-POW!
!
!
Roy Crane
SERVICE, INC.

"NO! NO!"

BANG!

By mistake, Teresa was shot down by one of her own bandits in trying to save Easy

"DOG! YOU 'AVE DEESOBEY MY ORDERS"

POW!

"ALL OF YOU 'AVE DEESOBEY! GO! GET OUT! DON' YOU DARE STEAL FROM THEES, MY PEOPLE!"

"AT LEAST WE GOT PART OF THE BOOTY, BOYS! HURRY!"

"THERE! DID I NOT SAY THIS WOULD HAPPEN? THEY ARE BANDITS AND TERESA OF THE GOLDEN VOICE IS THEIR LEADER. IN THE VILLAGE OF CASTATENANGO I LEARNED IT"

"FOR WHAT HAS HAPPENED, TERESA, WORDS CANNOT EXPRESS MY GRATITUDE, OR MY SORROW"

"I DO THEES BECOS I LIKE YOU, EASY. EES NOT MUCH. BETTER I DIE TO SAFE YOUR LIFE... THAN DIE ON GALLOWS... FOR MY CRIMES"

166

167

168

WHEN EASY AND HIS FRIENDS RETURN TO THE PLACE WHERE HE LEFT HIS PLANE:
BLAZES! LOOK!
IT'S BEEN DYNAMITED!
IT'S THE WORK OF THOSE BLINKING BANDITS!
NOW WE REALLY ARE IN A MESS!
HOW THE SAM HECK ARE WE GUNNER GIT BACK TO THE STATES?
THEY WALK TO THE GUATEMALAN COAST
AND THERE, BY GOOD FORTUNE, WASH FINDS A SEA CAPTAIN WHO OFFERS FREE PASSAGE TO NEW ORLEANS
AND BRING YOUR FRIENDS, SONNY. GLAD TO HAVE YE. GETS KIND OF LONESOME-JUST ME AN' MY TWO CATS ABOARD
OBOY! WAIT'LL I TELL EASY
HERE SHE IS, LADIES AND GENTLEMEN. SHIP-SHAPE AND READY TO GO
OBOY! WE AIN'T MAD AT ANYBODY!
WHO SAID CHRISTMAS COMES BUT ONCE A YEAR?
AND HERE'S THE CABIN. JUST MAKE YOURSELVES AT HOME
HEY! WHAT THE BLAZES!
!
HELP!
HELP!
DON'T BE ALARMED, SONNY. THERE'S NO DANGER. NOT THE SLIGHTEST

170

WOTTA YOU FEED THESE BEASTS?
WELL, BLESS MY SOUL! THAT REMINDS ME — I PLUMB FORGOT TO BUY ANY MEAT FOR LOVEY AND DOVEY
SNIFF
THAT'S THE LAST STRAW. FIRST YOU PROMISED YOU'D KEEP 'EM LOCKED UP, AND NOW —
BUT THE LOCK'S BUSTED
AT LEAST YOU CAN GO BACK TO LAND AND BUY SOME MEAT
NOW, DON'T YOU WORRY, MY DEAR SIR. LOVEY AND DOVEY ARE GENTLE AS LAMBS. I'LL GIVE THEM A BOWL OF OATMEAL
THEY DON'T SEEM TO LIKE OATMEAL
THAT'S FUNNY. THEY DID WHEN THEY WAS KITTENS. GETTIN' GROWED UP, I GUESS
BUT NEVER MIND. WE'LL REACH NEW ORLEANS IN A FEW DAYS. THEY'LL EAT OATMEAL IF THEY GET REALLY HUNGRY
YES, AND THEY MIGHT STICK TO A DIET OF RAW MEAT, MEANING US
MARK MY WORDS, THEY'S GUNNER BE TROUBLE!
SOMETHING'S GOT TO BE DONE!
THAT NIGHT:
MAYBE THEM PEOPLE'S RIGHT. LOVEY AND DOVEY'S GETTIN' SORTA CRANKY. I'LL SLIP INTO SAN MIGUEL BAY, WHILE EVERYBODY'S ASLEEP, AND BUY SOME MEAT

I BETTER BUY A NEW ROPE FOR THE ANCHOR, TOO, BEFORE -- GREAT SCOTT! IT'S BUSTED! THE BOAT'S DRIFTIN' OUT TO SEA!
MORNING:
WHERE'S THE CAPTAIN?
DOWN IN THE CABIN, I RECKIN. HE AIN'T ON DECK
THE BLAZES HE IS! I'VE JUST SEARCHED THE CABIN!
WELL, HE AIN'T ON DECK, THAT'S A CINCH
HE'S BOUND TO BE ON BOARD SOMEWHERE!
UNLESS —
THE TIGERS! MY STARS AN' GULLET! THEY'VE ET HIM ALIVE!
I KNOWED IT'D HAPPEN! THERE AIN'T EVEN A GUN ABOARD TO DEFEND OURSELVES! WHAT'LL WE DO?
NOW THAT THE TIGERS ARE WELL FED, THERE'S NO IMMEDIATE DANGER. WE'LL SIMPLY SAIL TO THE NEAREST LAND, AS THO NOTHING HAD HAPPENED
THAT'S ALL VERY FINE, EASY, EXCEPT FOR ONE THING— WHICH WAY IS LAND?
COPR. 1944 BY NEA SERVICE, INC.

WHEN CAPTAIN WIGGINS IS NOWHERE TO BE FOUND, THE PASSENGERS CONCLUDE THAT HE HAS BEEN EATEN BY HIS PET TIGERS, FOR WHICH HE FORGOT TO BUY FOOD
IN THAT CASE, THERE'S NOTHING TO WORRY ABOUT. THEY WON'T BE HUNGRY. SO WE'LL CALMLY SAIL WESTWARD AND-
BUT LOOK, EASY!
LOOK HOW THIN TH' TIGERS ARE! THEY WOULDN'T BE THAT THIN IF THEY'D JUST EATEN SOMEBODY
BLAZES! THAT'S RIGHT
!
THEY'RE STILL HUNGRY!
AND WHEN THEY'RE HUNGRY, THEY'RE VICIOUS!
LOOK OUT!
BLAZES! NOW WE ARE IN A MESS
I'LL SAY WE ARE! WE DASSN'T GO ON DECK TO SAIL THE SHIP!
AND IF WE CAN'T SAIL THE SHIP, HOW TH' HECK ARE WE GUNNA REACH LAND?

174

SHIPWRECKED — WELL, OF ALL THE BUM LUCK I EVER SEE!
SHUCKS! LULU BELLE, WE'RE LUCKY!
I'VE SEEN A HEAP WORSE PLACES THAN THIS FOR A SHIPWRECK. BESIDES, WE'RE JUST OFF THE COAST O' CUBA, AND IT'S ONLY A QUESTION O' TIME UNTIL WE'RE FOUND
PROBABLY THE ISLAND'S INHABITED ANYWAY. WE'LL GO EXPLORING, EACH OF US IN A DIFFERENT DIRECTION, AND MEET HERE AT SUNDOWN. OKAY?
SURE
MEANWHILE, ON THE CUBAN MAINLAND, NOT FAR AWAY:
I'M AN AMERICAN NEWSPAPER REPORTER OUT OF HAVANA, SIR—
AND YOU WEESH TO KNOW EEF THE WOLF-GIRL ACTUALLY EXISTS
HOW DID YOU GUESS?
EVERYBODY EEN PINAR DEL RIO EES TALKING ABOUT HER. FISHERMEN SAY THEY 'AVE SEEN A WOLF-GIRL ON GHOST ISLAND. THEY SAY SHE BARKS LIKE A DOG AND HOWLS AT THE MOON. WHAT NONSENSE! GHOST ISLAND HAS NOT BEEN INHABITED FOR FIFTEEN YEARS. THAT I KNOW

BUT THE MAN WHO LIVED THERE 15 YEARS AGO WAS A WIDOWER WITH TWO SMALL CHILDREN. SUPPOSEDLY, HE WAS LOST IN A STORM. THEN WHAT HAPPENED TO HIS CHILDREN? ISN'T IT POSSIBLE THAT ONE OF THEM SURVIVED? THAT SHE GREW UP ALONE, WILD, LIKE AN ANIMAL OF THE JUNGLE?
EES POSSIBLE, AMIGO, BUT HIGHLY IMPROBABLE. LAS' YEAR A FISHERMAN MYSTERIOUSLY DISAPPEARED AND I, MYSELF, SEARCHED GHOST ISLAND FROM END TO END—AND FOUND NOTHING!
"THE WOLF-GIRL OF GHOST ISLAND!" OH, WELL! IT'LL MAKE A GOOD STORY EVEN IF IT DOESN'T STAND UP!
ON GHOST ISLAND SITS A GIRL LITHE AS A PANTHER, HER HAIR FLOWING WILD AND FREE
SUDDENLY HER NOSTRILS QUIVER. SHE SNIFFS THE BREEZE LIKE A DEER
COPR. 1941 BY NEA SERVICE, INC.
S'FUNNY. I GOT A FEELIN' THAT SOMEBODY'S WATCHIN' ME!
ROY CRANE
OH, WELL! IT'S ONLY MY IMAGINATION, I GUESS. THERE'S NOTHIN' TO WORRY ABOUT
4-20

THA'S FUNNY! I'D OF SWORE I LAID MY CLOTHES ON THIS ROCK!
IF THIS IS YOUR IDEA OF A JOKE, YOU CLABBER-HEADED SLINKIN' JAILBIRD, I'LL LAM THE LIVING DAYLIGHTS OUTER YA!
WHAT THE BLAZES ARE YOU TALKING ABOUT?

YOU KNOW BLOOMIN' WELL WOT I'M TALKIN' ABOUT! YOU SNEAKED UP WHILE I WAS TAKIN' A BATH AN' STOLE ME CLOTHES!
THAT'S NOT MY STYLE, LULU BELLE, HONEST
THEN WASHIE DONE IT, DANG HIS HIDE! DON'T STAND THERE WITH YER MOUTH OPEN, YE BRAINLESS NINNY! DO SUMPIN! GO OUT TO TH' SHIPWRECK AN' GIT ME SUMPIN FITTEN TO WEAR
I'VE JUST BEEN OUT. SOMEBODY'S TAKEN EVERYTHING — EVEN THE FOOD AND BEDDING
MY STARS AN' BODY! THEN WOT ARE WE GUNNER EAT? WOT AM I GUNNER WEAR?
YOU CAN MAKE A DRESS OUT O' THE SAIL. BUT UNTIL THEN, I RECKON YOU'LL HAVE TO WEAR PART O' MY CLOTHES

MERCY SAKES! THESE PANTS IS SO TIGHT I DASSN'T SIT DOWN
AN' ME —A LADY— IN MAN'S CLOTHES! I WUZ NEVER SO MORTIFIED IN ME LIFE
WELL, HOW THE BLAZES YOU THINK I FEEL?
LISTEN HERE, EASY. I WOULDN'T PUT IT PAST WASH TO STEAL MY DUDS, BUT HE WOULDN'T OF STOLEN THE FOOD TOO — THEY'S SOMEBODY ON THIS ISLAND BESIDES US!
I KNOW. I FOUND A FISHING LINE TODAY, A VERY CRUDE ONE WITH A $20 GOLD PIECE FOR A SINKER.
$20 GOLD PIECE FER A SINKER? WHY, THEY MUST BE CRAZY!
NOBODY'S THAT CRAZY! WHOEVER'S ON THIS ISLAND, LULU BELLE, IS A SAVAGE!
MY STARS! THIS IS SERIOUS! MAYBE THA'S WHY LI'L WASHIE HASN'T COME BACK
HMM! I WONDER
HELP! HELP!
4-27 COPR. 1941 BY NEA SERVICE, INC.

IF THEY'S SAVAGES ON THIS ISLAND, THEN, BY GUPPY, IT'S HIGH TIME WE'RE FINDIN' OUT WOT HAPPENED TO LI'L WASHIE! HE SHOULD OF BIN BACK HOURS AGO
LOOK HERE
He who says wolf girl does not exist lies. I, Juan Garcia, have seen her. I am dying of blood poison cause by her spear. this day Nov 13 1939
WHAT NONSENSE! WHO EVER HEARD OF A "WOLF-GIRL"? IT'S PROB'LY ANOTHER JOKE!
WELL, I'M NOT SO SURE
MEANWHILE:
HEY, DON'T JUST SIT THERE. GET ME DOWN! DON'T YOU UNNERSTAND ENGLISH?
I'LL TRY AGAIN. PARLEZ VOUS FRANCAIS? ¿HABLA USTED ESPANOL? SPRECHEN SIE DEUTSCH? GET KNIFE--CHOP, CHOP!
WELL, AT LEAST SHE'S GONNA DO SUMPIN

May 1941

HEY!
WHAT'S TH' BIG IDEA?
LEGGO OF ME, YOU DIZZY DAME!
HELP!
EASY!
HELP!
YOO-HOOO! WASH-EEE! WHERE ARE YOU?
5-4
COPR. 1941 BY NEA SERVICE, INC.

? | **I'M GITTIN' WORRIED**

EASY AND LULU BELLE SEARCH THE ISLAND WHERE THEY WERE SHIPWRECKED FROM ONE END TO THE OTHER, LOOKING FOR WASH.
THEY FIND A SKELETON, A STRANGE SIGN TO BEWARE OF THE "WOLF-GIRL", AND OTHER THINGS, BUT NO WASH....

DON'T TURN YOUR HEAD, LULU BELLE, BUT LOOK IN THE BRANCHES OF THAT BIG CEIBA TREE

IT'S A GIRL! | YES, THE "WOLF-GIRL" WHO CAPTURED WASH. HOW DO I KNOW HE WAS CAPTURED? BECAUSE I FOUND **HER** FOOTPRINTS WHERE HIS ENDED

HUMPH! I DON'T TAKE NO STOCK IN THAT "**WOLF**-GIRL" STUFF. BUT WHOEVER SHE IS, SHE'S PRETTY. AND I'LL BET A COOKIE YOU'RE GREEN WITH ENVY BECAUSE SHE DIDN'T CAPTURE **YOU** INSTEADA LI'L WASHIE

NIX. IT'S BETTER TO CAPTURE THAN BE CAPTURED. **HEY!** THAT'S AN IDEA!

WOT'S AN IDEA? | **HURRY!** WE'LL CAPTURE THE "**WOLF**-GIRL"!

181

182

THERE'S ONLY ONE EXPLANATION WHY THE "WOLF-GIRL" HASN'T RETURNED TO HER CAVE, LULU BELLE — SHE KNOWS WE'RE HERE, WAITING TO GRAB HER
SHE DIDN'T SEE US
THEN HOW'D SHE FIND OUT?
SHE SMELLED US. I MEAN IT. SHE'S NO ORDINARY GIRL, LULU BELLE, SHE'S AN ANIMAL. YEARS AGO HER PARENTS MUST HAVE DIED, LEAVING HER TO GROW UP HERE ALONE. AND, LIKE AN ANIMAL, SHE DEVELOPED AN EXTREMELY KEEN SENSE OF SMELL AND HEARING
IT SOUNDS REASONABLE
ANOTHER THING. SHE'S CUNNING AND DANGEROUS. SHE'S CAPTURED WASH, AND NO TELLING WHAT SHE'S DONE WITH HIM. WHY, SHE MAY EVEN BE A CANNIBAL!
HUMPH!
WHAT'S MORE, SHE MAY BE WAITING TO AMBUSH US WHEN WE COME OUT
Wham!
WHAT'D I TELL YOU? THERE SHE GOES! COME ON, LULU BELLE! GRAB HER!

WHOA, YOU LITTLE WILDCAT! WHOA!
CRASH!
MY STARS! WOT HAPPENED?
GET ME OUT O' HERE. I FELL INTO A PIT. IT WAS COVERED WITH BRUSH AND I DIDN'T SEE IT. SHE LED ME PAST IT ON PURPOSE, TOO. BLAZES! HOW SHE COULD RUN!
HA HA HA!
YOU HEAR THAT? SHE'S LAUGHING AT ME!
OF COURSE SHE'S LAUGHIN' AT YOU! HAW, HAW! YOU WAS A SIGHT! THE DASHING ADVENTURER TRIES TO CAPTURE WOLF-GIRL AN' GITS CAUGHT HISSELF! HAW HAW HAW!
WELL! WHAT'S SO FUNNY ABOUT THAT?
LISTEN, EASY, THEY AIN'T BUT ONE WAY YOU'LL EVER CATCH THAT GAL. GIT SOME SENSE INTO YER PIN-HEADED NOODLE, STOP SCARING THE DAYLIGHTS OUTA HER, AN' START MAKIN' LOVE TO HER!
THINK IT OVER
5-18
COPR. 1941 BY NEA SERVICE, INC.

"I SAYS IT NOW AN' I'LL SAY IT AGAIN— YOU AIN'T GOT THE BRAINS YOU WAS BORN WITH"

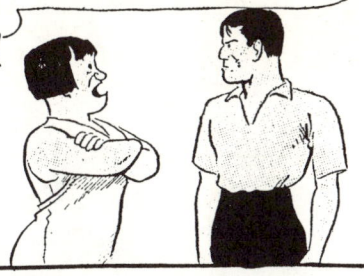

Easy is plenty worried. Wash, his buddie, has been captured by the so-called wolf-girl of Ghost Island. All his efforts to find Wash, or to catch the girl, have failed

"YOU AIN'T NOTHIN' BUT A GOL-DING MORON!"

"IS THAT SO!"

"YES, **THAT'S SO**! THE IDEA, TRYIN' TO CAPTURE A PORE LIL WOLF-GAL BY WHOOPIN' AN' YELLIN' AN' CHASIN' HER THRU THE WOODS LIKE A RAMPANT RHINOCEROS!"

"OKAY, BRIGHT-EYES, YOU SAY I OUGHT TO MAKE LOVE TO HER INSTEAD. BUT **HOW?** HOW THE BLAZES CAN A FELLA MAKE LOVE TO A GIRL WHO ISN'T HUMAN, WHO CAN'T EVEN TALK, AND RUNS LIKE A DEER IF YOU COME NEAR?"

"MY STARS AN' BODY! YOU, WHO'VE MADE GALS' HEARTS FLUTTER FROM BOMBAY TO TIMBUCTU, **YOU** AST **ME** HOW TO MAKE LOVE! **ME**, WHO IN 40 YEARS NEVER HAD NOBODY LOOK AT ME TWICE 'CEPTIN' THAT LOW-DOWN, TRIFLIN' C. HOLLIS WALLIS, AN' JO-JO, THE TATTOOED WONDER!"

"WELL, I'LL TELL YE **ONE** THING. THEY NEVER BUSTED THE HEART OF OLD TWO-FISTED LULU BELLE WI' A CLUB, BY GUPPY—THEY DONE IT SMOOTH AN' GENTLE, WI' CANDY AN' FLOWERS, TILL I PLUMB MELTED TO BUTTER"

THA'S THE WAY THEY DONE IT! AND I BETCHA THAT WOLF-GAL IS AS HUMAN AS ME, OR ANY BODY ELSE. USE YER HEAD, YOU LOP-EARED PELICAN! STOP SCARIN' THE DAYLIGHTS OUTA HER AN' TAKE HER A PRESENT
?
OKAY. I'LL TAKE HER SOME FLOWERS. I'LL EVEN MAKE A VASE TO PUT 'EM IN
NOW YER TALKIN'!
LATER:
FOR HOURS THE WOLF-GIRL SITS BESIDE THE CRUDE VASE OF FLOWERS, FONDLING IT, THINKING
THEN:
YOU AND YOUR SMART IDEAS! LOOK! A SPEAR!
THINGS DON'T LOOK SO GOOD, EASY, I'LL ADMIT. BUT LOVE DON'T ALWAYS COME SMOOTH AN' GENTLE. SOME-TIMES IT PLUMB RIPS YER HEART TO PIECES. IT HURTS! IT MAKES YOU MAD BECAUSE YOU DUNNO WOT'S AILIN'. TRY AGAIN, EASY. MAYBE IT'S A GOOD SIGN
Roy Crane
5-25 COPR. 1941 BY NEA SERVICE, INC.

"WHEN I RETURN FROM THE MAINLAND, I WILL HAVE A SURPRISE FOR YOU"

"YES, PAPA"

It was 15 years ago that the father of Maria and Josef Casablanca left in a leaky motorboat

There came a storm, and Papa Casablanca was never seen again

Miraculously, the girl survived, alone. As she grew older she forgot her name and how to talk, but she remembered such simple things as how to catch fish and to build a fire with flint and steel

"HI, YI! THE WOLF-GIRL!"

She learned to distrust and hate human beings. She became sly as a fox and wild as a deer

But since Easy has begun leaving flowers at her cave, she is troubled, bewildered

From afar, comes a strange and tantalizing odor

June 1941

187

FUDGE! I MADE IT OF SUGAR AN' THINGS WOT THE "WOLF-GIRL" TOOK FROM OUR SHIPWRECK. WE'LL LEAVE IT AT HER CAVE AN' SEE WOT HAPPENS
M-M-M!
AND TONIGHT, BY GUPPY, WE'LL SLEEP IN PEACE AN' SAFETY. THERE AIN'T NOBODY YET WHO EVER ET MY FUDGE WOT DIDN'T BECOME A FRIEND
BUT THIS "WOLF-GIRL" ISN'T LIKE OTHER PEOPLE, LULU BELLE. SHE'S CAPTURED WASH! SHE'S VICIOUS!
THA'S BECAUSE SHE GROWED UP WILD, AN' AIN'T NEVER HAD A MOTHER'S CARE AND AFFECTION, YE LOP-EARED NINNY! TREAT THE POOR, HOMELESS CHILD WI' LOVE AN' KINDNESS, AND TOMORROW MORNIN' I BETCHA THERE'S A RETURN GIFT FER US
CAUTIOUSLY, THE "WOLF-GIRL" EATS THE FUDGE. BUT WHY, SHE WONDERS, HAVE THESE CREATURES COME TO HER ISLAND? WHY MUST THEY BEWILDER HER? WHY CAN'T THEY LEAVE HER ALONE TO SWIM AND PLAY?
THAT NIGHT SHE SLIPS SILENTLY THRU THE JUNGLE
AND WHEN MORNING COMES:
MY STARS AN' BODY! WOT'S THIS?
A RETURN GIFT, OLD TOP. THE DEAR, MOTHERLESS CHILD IS EXPRESSING HER GRATITUDE FOR ALL WE'VE DONE!
6-1
Roy Crane
COPR. 1941 BY NEA SERVICE, INC.
WELL, WELL! FIRST WASH—AND NOW ALL THREE ARE CAPTURED!

YOU DON'T UNNERSTAND WIMMIN, THA'S THE TROUBLE WI' YOU! INSTEAD OF MAKIN' LOVE TO THAT POOR, MOTHERLESS WOLF-GIRL, OR WINNIN' HER CONFIDENCE WI' KINDNESS, YOU'VE SCARED HER. AND NOW LOOK WOT'S HAPPENED!!
SHUCKS! I HAVE A POCKETKNIFE. I'LL CUT THESE ROPES IN TWO— OR NEARLY IN TWO—
AND THEN....
!
EEK!
YOU LOP-EARED NINNY! DON'T YOU DARE HARM THAT POOR CHILD!
RECKON YOU WON'T SAVVY WHAT I'M SAYIN', MY LITTLE WILDCAT, BUT I'M GOING TO SAY IT ANYWAY

SHAME ON YOU! WE'VE TAKEN YOU GIFTS AND TRIED TO BE NICE —AND WHAT HAVE YOU DONE? YOU'VE CAPTURED MY BUDDIE, STOLEN OUR CLOTHES, TAKEN OUR FOOD, DROPPED ROCKS AT OUR HEADS, THROWN SPEARS AT US, AND TIED US TO TREES
BUT DESPITE ALL THAT, I'M NOT GOING TO HARM YOU, UNLESS—
UGH!
THAT SETTLES IT!
!
"STARTLED" IS A MILD DESCRIPTION OF THE WOLF-GIRL'S REACTION. DIM, FORGOTTEN MEMORIES OF 15 YEARS AGO SUDDENLY RETURN
HAVEN'T I TOLD YOU NOT TO PUT FROGS IN THE DRINKING WATER?
YES, PAPA
NOW YOU STAND THERE AND BEHAVE!
STAND THERE TILL YOU LEARN TO BEHAVE
YES, PAPA
PAPA?
WELL, MY STARS AND BUTTONS! AND I THOUGHT EASY DIDN'T KNOW NOTHIN' ABOUT WIMMIN!
?
?
6-8 COPR. 1941 BY NEA SERVICE, INC.

TERRY and the Pirates
by MILTON CANIFF

IN FULL COLOR!
The beautiful Sunday pages are now reprinted in full color with astonishing hues and pastels as only papers in those days did! This will be done in 12 quarterly volumes, hardcover, 11½x8½, each Sunday in its original size! Each volume: $35; subscription to 4: $99.

PAPERBACK EDITION
Going over all of Terry & The Pirates by Caniff once again in an affordable format! Each volume is 64 pp., 8½ x 11, color cover. The first volumes covering up to 1942 are out and a new one is issued every 3 months.
Vols. 1, 2 and past #5: $6.95; vols. 3-5: $5.95
Vols. 1-4 slipcased (1934-1937): $29.50
Vols. 5-8 slipcased (1937-1939): $29.50
Vols. 9-12 slipcased (1939-1941): $29.50
Vols. 13-16 slipcased (1941-1942): $29.50
SUBSCRIBE!
Get any 4 volumes past or future: $25, free P&H!

WE HAVE HUNDREDS OF VERY SATISFIED SUBSCRIBERS!

MISSING ANY VOLUMES?

FLYING BUTTRESS CLASSICS LIBRARY

Bill Blackbeard
Series Editor

The Complete 1924-1943
WASH TUBBS®
AND CAPTAIN EASY
by Roy Crane

Each volume of this quarterly reprint contains 192 pages of action of this classic which inspired so many action adventure strips. The complete reprint will take 18 volumes. Available in either a handsome gold-stamped hardcover with mounted art, or regular paperback.

Hardcovers: $32.50 each
Paperbacks: $16.95 each
ALL VOLUMES IN STOCK

SUBSCRIBE!
Only $80 for any 4 hardcovers ($130 separately)
Only $50 for any 4 paperbacks ($67.80 separately)

NBM
185 Madison Ave., Ste. 1502
New York, NY 10016